BREAD WINNER
BREAD BAKER

THE SECRET OF SUCCESS IS
NOT KEEPING SUCCESS A SECRET

*For Sheila
Another woman
creating her
own Destiny!
Love Sandy*

SANDY ELSBERG

First printing October 1997
Second Printing June 1999
Third Printing February 2001

ISBN 0-9709135-0-8
Published by Elleanna Press
30211 Avenida de las Banderas
Rancho Santa Margarita, CA 92688
tel. (888) 301-2922, fax (888) 301-4964
Printed in the United States of America

10 9 8 7 6 5 4 3 2

Cover design by Mike Fitts

ii

Contents

Dedication

This book is lovingly dedicated to...

Jerry Rubin,

for being my hero and my partner.
Jerry, you taught me so much: how not to be afraid,
how to own my life, how to put the passion, the purpose,
the power and the praise into everyday life.
You have truly given new meaning to the words,
"free radical"—I love and miss you.

John Milton Fogg,

whose wonderful book about the *Greatest Networker in the World* inspired me to write about another ultimate networker, this time from a woman's point of view.
Perhaps the thing we most seek in our relationships is not only to be heard, but also to be known.
Thank you, John, for knowing me, even before I knew myself.

Special Thanks...

I would also like to thank some of the special angels who have brought magic to my life and joy to my journey, including:

Susan Fogg, whose friendship has empowered me in ways that only a true woman of power can empower other women, and whose crystal clear vision has held up a mirror for me.

Tony Rich, who, in one of many moments of brilliance, gave me the title of *Bread Winner Bread Baker,* along with the joy of his friendship.

Morty & Eleanor, my first and greatest mentors—truly the most natural Networkers I've ever known—my father, who has never waited for wealth to become a philanthropist, my mother, whose very presence left people feeling lighter, brighter and happier with themselves. They taught me that humor and kindness are the greatest healers, and they brought more gifts to my life than there are stars in the sky.

My wonderful sister, *Stacey,* brother *Bradley* and my brother-in-law, *Bob McAdams,* whose unconditional kindness and support continue to make it possible for me to do what I do, be who I am, and have the wonderful, abundant life that I have. Thank you for always, always, always being there for me.

Bill and Gert Elsberg, my dear fairy godparents, whose caring and credit cards have made it possible for me, not only to "go to the ball," but also learn how to throw my own party and earn my own royalty.

Bill, who taught me my own true strength, and to whom I owe the most precious gifts in my life...

our children, *Eleah and Anna,* who bring laughter, balance and meaning to my every moment.

All of my special friends, helpers, guardians, rescuers and sup-porters—upline, downline and all around my world—who would fill the pages of another book if I named you all. May God bless you for honoring my life with your courage, kind-ness, thoughtfulness and spirit of celebration and contribution.

And to all of my great goddess mentors, the uncommon women whose higher ground is their power to create. This magnificent league of "Angels with Ovaries" includes the likes of Mother Teresa, Oprah Winfrey, Jane Fonda, Barbra Streisand, Bette Midler, Rosa Parks, Mary Kay, Terry Cole-Whittaker, Golda Meir, Princess Diana, Lucille Ball, Gloria Steinham, Marianne Williamson, Alice Walker, Maya Angelou, Eleanor Roosevelt, Harriet Tubman, and others too numerous to count. Each of them, in her own way, has put on her steel breastplate and horned helmet to take up her spear and wield the transforming power of love. Collectively, they give permission to all authen-tic warriors to use the power of their anger as well as their com-passion, their strength as well as their vulnerability, their wit, wisdom, talent and humility to manifest positive change in the world. I am truly your devoted groupie.

—B'virkat Shalom

Foreward

"My father taught me that the very best teachers were those who enabled their students to surpass them.

Sandy Elsberg told me that she 'went to school' on my book, *The Greatest Networker in the World*. Based on how good this book is, I'd say I've become a very good teacher indeed!

When I finished reading *Bread Winner Bread Baker*, I knew, with complete and pleased conviction, I could do this business: I know why and I know how and I believe beyond any shadow of doubt I'll be successful. I'll bet you'll feel the same way.

Sandy's a teacher—the best. And she can teach you how to be successful. And because she is one of those rare 'best teachers,' chances are very good she'll teach you to surpass her. And that—given who Sandy is and all she's accomplished—is the tallest of tall orders.

If you're up for learning how to be the Bread Winner and the Bread Baker—and have more fun doing it than you ever imagined—your teacher is waiting on the pages of this compelling and utterly wonderful book."

—John Milton Fogg
Editor of Upline®
Author of *The Greatest Networker in the World*

Introduction

In the story you are about to read, *Bread Winner Bread Baker,* you'll meet a character called "the Bag Lady." No, I'm not the Bag Lady, yet you will see a lot of me in her, and a lot of her in me—at least I hope so.

I created the Bag lady to represent the finest qualities of the best people I've known in Network Marketing. She's a woman who loves her dreams and empowers others to believe in their own. By transcending her personal hardships and failures, she's created her own success and destiny through a wonderful alchemy of honesty and love, passion and action.

She's part Helen Keller...

"Life is either a bold adventure or nothing at all."

Part Mary Pickford...

"Failure is not in the falling down, but in the staying down."

And part Mother Theresa...

"I am only the pencil in the hand of a writing God, sending a love letter to the world."

She is a Bread Winner and a Bread Baker; a nurturer, a gardener, a provider and a warrior. (And, on top of all that, she's got great taste in handbags!). And you know what? If you listen to what she has to say and put your own passion into action, I think that you'll discover that there's a lot of the Bag Lady in you!

I wrote this book because I wanted to give something back to an industry that has so richly rewarded me for believing in its limitless possibilities. I wanted to write a book that would clearly demonstrate that Network Marketing really does allow ordinary people to do extraordinary things, to create more love in the world while creating more abundance in their lives. To make a living by making a difference. To do well by doing good.

People often ask me the secret of my success. But that's just what it's NOT! It's not a secret! In Network Marketing, the secret to success is *not* keeping your success a secret!

The whole point of this business is to duplicate your success, to teach others everything you possibly can to help them achieve their goals. Because every time you help someone climb their mountain, you get closer to the top of the mountain yourself. Some of the most important work to do is an "inside job," making yourself a master copy worth duplicating.

Gandhi was once asked to put into a single sentence what message he wanted to share with the world. He answered, "My life is my message."

That's also the Bag Lady's most important message, to live a life that embodies your values, your deepest beliefs and your highest goals. If you do, then all of your actions become an expression of your passion, and your life becomes joyful and abundant. And when you radiate joy and abundance, people will be attracted to you. People will follow you.

Imagine a world where work is play...

Imagine a world where no one has to compete with anyone else to enjoy complete sufficiency...

Imagine a world where ordinary people can make their dreams come true, and gladly teach others to do the same...

When you can imagine it—you can create it. You can have a life that is truly the embodiment of an idea expressed by Kahlil Gibran:

"Work is love made visible."

Are you ready for that kind of success?
Good. Now, let's meet the Bag Lady.

Sandy Elsberg
Maui, Hawaii

CHAPTER ONE

Introducing...the Bag Lady

It was raining as she stood on the corner of 44th and 6th Avenue, her arm confidently raised in the universal salute of all New Yorkers in search of taxis—Lady Liberty sans torch. She took in the old familiar street smells: damp and dirty sidewalks, smokey buses and over-baked pretzels. Ah, April in Manhattan. Some things hadn't changed in the 22 years since she'd called New York home.

It had been a busy day: first, the meeting with the producers of the Reggis and Chrissy Lee Show; a working lunch with her publisher—two books down, one to go; a capability presentation at the promotion firm...Only the last had been less than perfect.

She was considering people to help her market her new video series. The owner/president had been most charming, and the agency's work was both clever and glitzy. But one thing she knew to look for very quickly was depth— or the lack of it. This outfit's work was much like its leader: all style, little substance. Next.

Out of the corner of her eye, she noticed a young woman about 15 feet away desperately waving for a cab-driver's attention. "Who claimed the corner first?" she wondered, and smiled at the natural return of her New Yorker ethics. It didn't matter. There was no hurry.

Her meetings were finished and her only further obligations were to her stomach and taste buds—in that order— and both of them certainly could wait. However, her cramped aching feet longed to make a break for it, escaping those beautifully crafted leather pumps. Sexy and stylish they might be, but she was no longer accustomed to high heels for eight-hour stretches. She spent most of her days in faded-friendly jeans and sneakers, working from her home, which overlooked the beach in Maui.

She was, she liked to say, "unemployable." It was true. At some important, but forgotten moment somewhere, some time long ago, her entrepreneurial spirit had literally over-taken her. She was, now and forever, destined to work for the greatest boss in the world. Herself.

And it was apparent to even the most casual observer, things were going well. From the look of her expertly tailored Italian raincoat to her impressive, though understated, jewelry—"All...," she would delightedly add, "...at wholesale, Dahling." Very well indeed.

As if summoned, a streak of lit-up yellow careened 'round the corner and squealed to a stop with a splash in front of her. By reflex she reached for the door, then remembered the woman in the baggy brown coat.

"Where are you headed?" she asked, turning toward her. The other woman's defeated body language spoke louder than her weary voice.

"Penn Station. Thirty-third." She answered with a heavy sigh, clearly not expecting an answer.

"Want to share?"

The woman in brown hesitated, as if not sure what to say. She had never shared a cab with anyone in New York before. But then she thought of the baby-sitter, angrily watching the clock, and accepted without complaint.

"Thanks," she mumbled, absently, eyes downcast, sliding with effort across the back seat. "Where are you going?" she asked.

"I'm staying at the Plaza. It's the opposite direction, I know, but there's no sense standing in the rain—is there? We'll drop you off. I'm not in any hurry."

"Thanks," the young woman said, cautiously perking up just a little. "I really appreciate this. My baby-sitter will be furious as it is. She has night school and I'm already 30 minutes late and I'm sure she's going to quit and if she does, I don't know what..." and the rest slipped into silence as she stared out the watery window.

After instructing the driver where and who first, the two women settled into their midtown journey for the long ride through the parking lot of traffic. In Manhattan, rush hour plus rain equaled gridlock. It's the law of the concrete jungle.

"Why do we park on our driveways and drive on parkways?" the older woman quipped, and as she did, she dove into a big—humongous is more accurate—black bag the size and shape of a postman's pouch. The bag was black Italian leather, buttery soft and polished to a soft sheen. Gorgeous. Absolutely stunning. And it looked loaded.

She pulled out an equally expensive looking day planner and started making notes. Meanwhile, the girl in the baggy-brown sat slumped in the corner of the cab, sporting an attitude worse than the wet weather.

The woman with the bag looked up, the Jewish mother in her now alert and awakened at the sight of her companion's more than forlorn expression.

"So, Dearie. You're not happy?" Her tone—part question, part observation, part challenge—gave her away immediately. You can take a girl out of New York, but...

"Bad day," the young woman answered, in a flat, tight voice.

"Bad day?" responded the woman with the bag, clearly warming to the challenge. "Bad day? Sweetheart, my mother taught me that every day above ground is a good day. You're above the ground—yes? So, what could be so bad?"

The young woman was silent, clearly debating whether to open up or stay shut down—safe and sad. She was holding back tears, but not very successfully.

"Listen, Dahling," the lady with the bag said, gently resting one diamond sparkling hand on the arm of the brown coat beside her. "What did you say your name was...?"

"Dana."

"Listen, Dana. I don't want to upset you. I can see you're not in the best of spirits. But, can we talk? I'm a professional listener."

"Oh…it won't do any good." the young woman responded with a stuttering sigh. "I'm beyond hope—really!"

The tears welling in her eyes had reached critical mass. The dam burst and with it a sudden deluge of words.

"You know, I try! I try and try so hard to do what's right. But nothing ever goes my way. I just feel like such…such a failure!" She paused for a gulp, leaving her stinging self-indictment hanging. "Failure…" A warm hand wrapped itself around hers—silent, strong, reassuring.

She continued, "All those rotten things he said about me. My ex, I mean," she turned now facing her companion. "Maybe he was right. Maybe I am useless. Stupid. I've been all over this city today. Nobody will give me a job. Nobody! And why would they? I don't know how to do anything—except take care of my kids."

"And I'm not sure I'm any good at that, to tell you the truth. Little Kevin's always sick lately. Probably because I always keep the heat turned way down to save money. And Katie has asthma. I have no insurance, of course, so I can't come up with the money to have her tested for allergies. My rent is way past due and I'm sure the landlord will kick us out any day now. Oh, and my dinosaur of a car just became extinct last week. It's hopeless! I'm hopeless!"

"I don't know what to do…"

She was sobbing now, her whole body—along with about 50 pounds of excess weight she carried around with her, one problem per pound—heaved heavily with emotion.

Suddenly there was an unmistakable ripping sound as the strained seams of her raincoat gave way. Startled, she stopped crying. Realizing what had happened, Dana furtively looked over at her companion to see if she had noticed. The other woman smiled back at her with a sly twinkle, and in an instant, they were both giggling like school girls.

"Okay. I get it. You're not happy."

"Wait a minute. I have just the thing for you...," said the older woman as she dove deep into her big black bag.

Triumphantly she emerged and handed Dana a—yes, that's what it was—a white plastic wall-light switch.

"Here," she offered, "if you're not happy, just flip the switch!"

Dana was momentarily at a loss for words. She looked over with an expression of delight mixed with confusion.

"You'll pardon me for resorting to visual aids, Dahling," said the woman putting on her garment center accent. "I taught first graders for 10 years. Dick and Jane, meet Dana," she said with a smile.

"I'm serious." she said, fixing her eyes on Dana with gentle power.

"Right now you feel your life is out of control. Frankly, most things in life are not in your control anyway. Except for one thing: Your thoughts. Nobody—and I do mean nobody—gets to put anything into your head, Dana, without your complete permission."

She had Dana's total attention now.

"And do you know what? Whatever's in your mind is in your life. That's a fact. I'm living proof."

Dana looked down at the light switch she was holding. "Ma'am," she began apologizing, "I don't mean to be rude, but you're obviously not hurting for money. It's a little hard to think positive when you're raiding your kid's piggy bank to buy food for a day."

The woman smiled. "You know, Dana, that reminds me of something Mahalia Jackson—one of the all time great gospel singers—once told me. She said it was easy to be independent when you've got money, but to be independent when you haven't got a thing, that's the Lord's true test.

"I know, right now you think you're the only one in the world who's ever felt this hopeless. The reason I know that is because I've felt the very same way. I've been where you are."

"You're kidding."

"It was only about eight years ago."

"So, what happened? How did you turn your life around?"

"It's a long story. I'll give you the Cliff Notes version for now," the woman answered, turning to face Dana full front, her most comfortable storytelling position.

"My world was a total shambles. I was a little older than you are now and eight months pregnant with my second daughter. My older child was five at the time. It was a high risk pregnancy and, like you, I had no insurance. I actually had to go and apply for public assistance, can you believe it,...welfare for heaven's sake, because my doctor had turned me away. No kidding, 'Get out,' until I came up with the $2,000 I owed her."

"Can you imagine? I told her I didn't have $2,000. I told her I didn't have two of anything!"

Dana was caught up in the story now. She was beginning to like this woman—a lot.

"I was truly desperate. $250,000 in debt. And how could I get a job—my ankles were the size of a normal woman's thighs! I was 100 pounds overweight! Try job hunting in that condition. Hello!"

"I'd been using my credit cards to buy groceries, but they were all maxed out. My husband was very sick, chronically ill. He couldn't work. Some days just taking a shower wore him out to exhaustion. Dear man. He couldn't help. Imagine, I'd found Prince Charming, but he was the one asleep in the woods!"

"I had no one to turn to. No one. My soon-to-be-born baby and I were trapped together in a body that couldn't support either of us—or anyone else. To say my life simply wasn't working didn't even work!"

Dana had come out of her slumped position and was now leaning markedly toward her companion, completely focused on every word she was hearing.

"I knew something had to give. For those two whole eternal hours sitting in that ice-cold welfare office, there was this firestorm frenzy going on in my head. Rage was just building moment by moment; my pride was wounded beyond imagining!"

"And then, my switch flipped..."

"What happened?" Dana couldn't wait to hear.

"Something just broke free inside me. A little, yet surprisingly powerful voice inside said, 'No. No thank you. This is not good enough for me and my family. I do not choose this. No thank you!' And I got up, and I handed the papers back to the lady at the desk and I walked out of there, and I never, ever looked back."

Dana, completely caught up in the story, wanted more. "But what did you do?"

The woman gazed out the window, sizing up the traffic. "We haven't moved in at least 10 minutes—have we? Looks like I just might have time to tell you the rest. But what about your baby-sitter? How much trouble are you in by now?"

The baby-sitter! Dana had completely forgotten how late she was.

"Oh, wow, you're right! I should at least call. But..., it'll have to wait 'till I get to a phone booth at Penn Station."

"Tell you what...," the woman volunteered, as she began searching through her bag, quickly producing a small, dark gray gadget and handing it to Dana. "This phone goes everywhere with me. Speed dialing is my favorite form of exercise..." She winked. "Next to lifting a fashionable fork to my mouth. "Put it to good use while we're stuck here playing lost tourists. Call your sitter and then let's talk. What's the number?" She quickly dialed the sleek little phone and handed it over to Dana.

Dana finished her call quickly. This time, the baby-sitter was unusually understanding. She handed the phone back to the woman who returned it to her bag.

"That's really something," Dana commented, looking down at the impressive big black bag.

The woman beamed. "It's my trademark. This bag goes everywhere with me—and I do mean everywhere! Some of my friends call me, 'the Bag Lady.' Don't you love it?"

"It's wonderful." Dana smiled warmly. "Please, go on with your story."

"Well, did you ever hear the expression, 'When the student is ready the teacher appears'?" Dana shook her head no.

"Well, that's the way the Universe works. Trust me. When you start paying more attention to things other than your problems you'll notice it's true. The very next day I was giving a massage to a woman client of mine—that's how I was managing to make a little money back then—and she was telling me about this business she had just started. It was in something called 'network marketing;' have you heard of it?" Dana shook her head no again.

"She seemed so happy with how well her business was going, and then, to my utter amazement, she offered to help me start my own!

"I asked her how much she was making, and she told me it was her second month in business and she was expecting a check somewhere in the neighborhood of $4,000 to $7,000! I was floored. I said $7,000! That's the right neighborhood for me!

"So, I took her up on her offer. Set my goal for my first month's commission check at $7,000. I figured since she already knew how to do that, she could teach me to do it, too. I just knew I could do it."

"And did you?" Dana just couldn't wait to hear.

"No...," the Bag Lady admitted, with a melodramatic sigh. Then, coming right back in triumph, "My first check covered the delivery of my baby and all my unpaid doctor bills. I also sold enough products in those first four weeks to buy a crib, a stroller and feed my family during that first month. I knew I was well on my way out of debt. And—you'll love this," she gleamed, putting her hand on Dana's for emphasis, "my first check arrived on the day after my baby did!"

"That's when I got it, Dana. I really got it. And my life was changed forever."

An amazed "Wow!" followed by thoughtful silence was all Dana could manage at that moment.

For some minutes there was quiet in the cab. Dana stared out the window, her thoughts tumbling over one another as the Bag Lady's story sank in.

Dana noticed they had inched all the way to 35th Street. Only two more blocks. She could easily get out and walk from here, she thought. "No, don't," said the voice in her head.

It would be much faster. "No." The voice again.

She was telling herself to stay, to take advantage of the little bit of time she had left with this extraordinary woman.

Time was running out. Dana mustered the courage to ask, "Do you think I could do something like that? Could I do what you did?"

The Bag Lady smiled warmly and dove back down into her big bag. She pulled out a small brass picture frame and held it towards Dana.

"Only if you want to, Dana. But understand this, I'm not just talking about 'Want To.' You've wanted to for years—am I right?"

Dana nodded, agreeing, but not really understanding.

"The Universe always takes you at your word, Dana. As long as you 'want to,' you'll keep wanting to. Not having, just wanting. Do you see?"

Dana nodded, agreeing again, and beginning to understand.

"I'm talking about burning desire, Dana—the kind that keeps your heart yearning and your mind turning while you sleep. The kind that wakes you up at the crack of dawn, because you can't wait to get to work! I'm talking about passion, Dana. Passion!"

"Here." She handed the ornate little picture frame to Dana. "You decide who you really, really are going to be. See yourself as that person you are passionate about becoming. Picture yourself—not off in the future—but now, today, as who you want to be for yourself and your family, and put that picture in this frame. That's the first step to changing your life for the better forever!

"You know," the Bag Lady continued, "a very wise and dear person always used to say to me, 'See your future, then work backward.' And that's what it's time for you to do, Dana."

Dana's mind was scrambling now. This was an important moment for her. She knew that. She could feel gears shifting into place. Something was different. She felt good for the first time in weeks—months. She couldn't let this chance get away.

"Will you help me?" she blurted, amazed at herself.

The cab pulled up to the curb next to the building where Gimbels Department Store once stood. Penn Station was right underneath it.

"I'll be in town for 10 days," the Bag Lady said. "I have some business to take care of, and I'm also spending some time with family here in the area. Think about what we've talked about, Dana. Think very hard about what kind of a commitment you're willing to make to have the life you've dreamed of.

"I'll be staying at the Plaza. Call me if you want to talk some more." She jotted the number on her business card and handed it to Dana.

Dana hurriedly gathered her belongings, along with the Bag Lady's gifts—the light switch and the picture frame—and put them in her purse. She paid the cabdriver and tipped him as much as she could manage, still having just enough money for the train home.

She looked the Bag Lady directly in the eyes—something she rarely did, noticing that it felt good—extended her arm, shook her hand firmly, and said in a voice that didn't seem quite her own, "Thank you so much. I won't forget what you said. You will hear from me." And she smiled in a strongly felt, self-assured way that she realized she hadn't done for a long, long time.

Dana raced down the stairwell leading to Penn Station. She rushed across the bustling terminal through the turnstiles, more than relieved to see the train, already partially loaded with passengers, waiting for her. She slid into a seat, her mind still racing from her conversation with the Bag Lady.

In the manner of all subway passengers everywhere, her eyes automatically drifted to the advertising panels just above the windows inside the train. An ad for a popular sneaker company suddenly caught her eye and the headline slammed itself into her mind.

"JUST DO IT."

"Yes!" said the voice in Dana's head. "Yes!"

Chapter Two
Picture This

D ana opened her apartment door with "Just Do It!" sneakers still running 'round in her mind. "Just do it. Do it. Do it. Do It!" was all she could think about. She was replaying her conversation with the Bag Lady over and over. What if it was true? What if she really could change her whole life, starting now, today?

She stepped into a living room of chaos. Wendy, the baby-sitter, was already wearing her coat and moving out the door. "The baby's had his dinner, but not his bath. Katie has more homework to finish. There's a note from her teacher on the table. See ya tomorrow." Whoosh! Wendy disappeared before Dana could even say good night.

In a flash, four-year-old Katie gleefully wrapped herself around Dana's leg. "Mommy's home! Color with me, Mommy. Will you please color with me? Please?"

Suddenly aware of his mother's arrival, baby Kevin immediately started to scramble out of his high chair. He was covered in tomato sauce and several strands of spaghetti hung from the once-golden ringlets on his head. In an instant, all thoughts of her fascinating cab ride vanished. Dana attended to her children.

It wasn't until later, when the baby was safely tucked in for the night and she sat on the floor coloring with Katie, that Dana remembered the picture frame. She dug both the frame and the light switch out of her purse and brought them over to the crayon-covered coffee table. She cleared a space and set the picture frame up, so that its empty center faced her.

"Why isn't there any picture, Mommy?" Katie wanted to know.

"Because it's waiting for us to put one in, Honey." Dana answered, as much to herself as her daughter.

"I'll do it, Mommy. I'll make a picture for it—okay?"

"Sure, baby. That's a good idea. Why don't you draw a picture of Mommy. Would you do that for me?"

Katie was delighted! She tackled her assignment with determined relish. As her daughter's chubby fingers wrestled the fat red crayon into submission, Dana's mind returned to the Bag Lady. "Picture yourself in the future you dream of today." That's what she had said. Wasn't it?

Dana looked wistfully around the room. There were some things about this happy mess she wouldn't trade for any amount of money. Active, happy children lived here. The evidence was everywhere and overwhelming. "That's just fine with me," Dana thought.

But there sure was lots of room for improvement. And most of it required cash—or credit—neither of which she had. If she could only find a job. But that was going to mean leaving the kids with a sitter a lot more of the time. She really hated that idea.

"How's this, Mommy? See, I drew a picture of you!"

Katie had drawn Dana in red, her favorite color and Katie's, too. The Mommy in the picture had strong, powerful stick arms that stood straight out from her sides, spider fingers outstretched, as if ready to grab onto all she could hold. There was a wonderful, huge ball of bright yellow over her right shoulder, from which sunbeams stretched extravagantly running off both sides of the paper. But the most impressive thing about the woman in the picture was her smile, a bold, broad semi-circle of color that filled up her entire face.

Dana gazed at the picture speechless for a moment. Staring at her daughter's drawing, she realized she was in love with the woman in the picture. Was this the way her daughter saw her? Powerful, happy, beaming with light.

In that moment Dana decided, if Katie could see her that way, then it was time she started seeing herself that way, too!

"This is absolutely beautiful, Katie," Dana said. "This is the best picture of me that anyone could ever make. Thank you, Sweetheart. Thank you."

She carefully positioned the drawing inside the frame. Then she put both arms around Katie and hugged her, swaying gently back and forth for a very long time.

Somewhere in mid-hug, somewhere in her head, Dana suddenly heard something! What was it? What was that sound? It was...It was—"Click." That's what it was.

"Click"—just like a light switch.

CHAPTER THREE

The Inside Job

The next morning, at 8:00 A.M., the phone rang in the Bag Lady's suite at the Plaza. She'd gotten up two hours before and had already showered, breakfasted and checked her voice mail and email. When Dana's call rang through, she was snugly wrapped up in a grand looking armchair in the sitting room. She had just begun to wade into a wonderful new book on personal growth.

"Please, tell me what to do next," Dana's voice demanded through the phone, forgetting all politeness.

"Well, good morning to you, too, Dahling!" The Bag Lady replied, accent in full swing. "You're Dana from the cab—am I right?" She had spoken to literally dozens of people since her taxi conversation with Dana, but she was a virtuoso of the telephone and rarely, if ever, forgot a voice.

"Yes. Oh. I'm sorry I was rude. Good morning. Good morning to you, too," Dana answered, clearly more than a little embarrassed.

"It's good to hear from you again, Dana. So tell me, did you survive the wrath of your stood-up baby sitter?"

"No..., well..., yes. Actually, it wasn't so bad. I've been thinking a lot about what you said. To tell the truth, I haven't thought about anything else. I barely slept. I've just *got* to know how to do what you did. Will you help me, please?"

"Well, that depends. 'Got-to' is pretty good. Are you sure you don't mean, 'want-to?' Remember that old Indian chief, Gottawanna. Make sure you gotta more than you wanna. I don't waste my time with anyone who doesn't, not anymore."

"But I *do* want to. I mean, I've got to, more than you can possibly know. Please tell me what to do."

"I can't promise it will happen for you overnight, or in a month, or even in a year. I *can* promise you we'll start putting cash in your pocket right away, maybe even today. But, Dana, I'm looking for people who are willing to go for the four-year degree. Are you sure you're ready to work for your MBA?" The Bag Lady paused to chuckle. "Relax, we're not talking Harvard MBA; we're talking *my* MBA—Massive Bank Account."

"Oh." Dana laughed. "You don't know how ready! When do we start?"

"How fast can you get here?" the Bag Lady countered.

One hour later, Dana was at the door of the Bag Lady's suite. "What do we do first?" she asked as she walked through the door, foregoing small talk. She was clearly anxious to jump right in.

"First, I suggest we—meaning you—sit down," said the Bag Lady and following her own advice, she sat. Dana perched herself on the edge of a tufted armchair, opposite her new mentor.

"The first thing we're going to do, Dana, is work on you."

Immediately self-conscious and embarrassed, Dana looked down at the clothes she was wearing.

"Listen," Dana said, "I know I'm not exactly dressed for success. I ran out the door in such a hurry and I don't have much of a wardrobe, but I know I can do better than this."

"I'm not talking about your clothes, Dahling. That's just the window dressing. The outside will take care of itself in good time. Changing your life is first an inside job."

"I'm not sure I understand," Dana questioned.

"Let me ask you something: When I look at you, I see something absolutely great. What do you think is absolutely great about you?"

Dana was clearly stumped. She was thinking she couldn't be very great to have gotten her life into such a mess. "Umm," was all she could offer.

"Okay, I'll tell you." the Bag Lady said, rescuing her new friend. "You made a very big, very scary decision today, a decision most people wouldn't be willing to make. Oh, they might want the same thing you do, but not badly enough to put down the remote and turn off the TV."

"You also made a huge commitment today, that even fewer people are willing to make. They don't want to take the risk of failing. You see what I'm getting at? What you did today took courage!"

"I guess I didn't see that."

"That's right! And that's what we're going to work on." The Bag Lady reached into her bag, which, not surprisingly, was right by her side. "Here. It's time to change the tape." And she handed Dana an audio cassette.

Dana turned the tape in her hand, looking for the label.

"Don't bother." The Bag Lady answered her unspoken question. "I recorded that tape myself."

"What's on it?" Dana wanted to know.

"Before I tell you what..., let me tell you why."

"Think back to our cab ride yesterday, the part when you where telling me about all the things that were wrong with your life. Do you happen to remember any of the words you used to describe yourself?"

Dana poked through her memory for fragments of their conversation. Strangely, she couldn't recall much of anything she had said. The only words she remembered were the Bag Lady's.

"I can see you're coming up blank. Maybe I can help you. Does the word 'failure' sound familiar? How about these: 'worthless...' 'stupid...' 'hopeless...?'"

"Oh yeah. I guess I did use those words," Dana remembered—ruefully.

"Dana, I don't mean to pry into your spiritual beliefs, but do you happen to believe in a Higher Power?"

"Oh yes. I'm not exactly what you'd call religious, but I do believe in God."

"And do you believe that this God of yours created you along with all the other beings on this planet?"

"Of course."

"Well, you don't seem to be giving God much credit. I can't imagine that any self-respecting God would go around creating hopeless, useless, stupid failures. Am I right?" the Bag Lady challenged.

"I see your point. But I wasn't putting the blame on God. I wasn't putting the blame on anyone, but myself."

"Wonderful! That's an excellent policy—taking responsibility for what's in your life. You're a rare bird, indeed! And do you see how much power that gives you? Because, if you had the ability to create it, you also have the ability to change it! Right?"

"Yes. Right. That's why I'm here with you."

"Great! So, the first things we're going to work on are those foul, self-defeating words in your head. Now, I want to show you something."

The Bag Lady rose and went over to the night stand and brought back a water pitcher and a glass. "Do me a favor, Honey, go get me a can of cola out of the service-bar over there." As Dana eagerly complied, the Bag Lady looked all around the room, searching for something. She let out a satisfied, 'Ah' and quickly removed the fruit from a large crystal bowl on the ornate side-board.

She brought the bowl back to where they were sitting and placed it on the small table between them. Then she placed a glass of water in the bowl. Now she dove back into her bag and retrieved an ordinary eye dropper.

"Okay, we're ready. Would you open that can of soda for me, please?"

Dana opened the can and handed it to her companion.

"Now, Dana, think back. Tell me one time when you were a child that something happened or someone said something to you that caused you to feel really bad about yourself."

Dana didn't have to think for long.

"There was a party when I was in the seventh grade," she said, excited with her remembrance. "It was the first one that the boys were invited to. We were dancing to records. All of my friends had gotten new dresses for the party, but my dad was drinking heavily back then, and there was no money in our house for new clothes. I remember standing alone at one point and several of the girls were in a huddle nearby, whispering. Every now and then they'd look over at me and giggle. I knew they were talking about my old dress. I just knew it."

"Wow," the Bag Lady said in a soft voice, "that was a tough one. I can see it left a lasting impression." She dipped the eye dropper into the cola can and then deposited one drop of the brown liquid in the glass of clear water.

"You see, Dana, this glass of clear water is like the pure little child's mind you came into this life with. That mind believed anything was possible. That mind believed you were perfect, just the way you were. But experiences like the one you just described are toxic. That toxicity comes from other people's guilt or shame being projected on you. And you see how just this one little drop of cola made the color of the water just a bit darker—it doesn't take much to poison a mind either. Think of another example."

Dana thought. "Well…, my brothers and sisters always used to tease me about being fat. It's kind of funny, because I know I'm fat now, but I wasn't back then. They were all younger and sort of skinny, so my mom told me to just ignore them. But she still gave me those disapproving looks whenever I reached for a second piece of toast or anything."

The Bag Lady squirted another drop of cola into the glass. The water darkened a little more.

"More poison. You see how those experiences have colored your thinking? And what about those things you told me your ex-husband said? They obviously left an impression." She added yet another drop, then another. The water was turning amber.

"This is what you're up against, Dana. So, you have to learn how to clean up your act. Your mind is stained with negative thoughts, self criticism, doubtful voices from your past. We need to get your mind back to its original, clear, pure state."

As she spoke, she was slowly pouring clean water from the pitcher into the glass containing the water and cola.

"Imagine this clear water in the pitcher is the work you do on yourself: self improvement books, motivational tapes, seminars, support groups, whatever helps you most."

The glass sitting in the bowl began to overflow, but the water inside was still not clear. Still the Bag Lady continued pouring. Neither woman spoke. Half the contents of the water pitcher had already been poured into the overflowing glass and still the liquid was clouded. It wasn't until the pitcher was nearly empty that the once amber stain became undetectable and clear.

"You see, Dana, it only takes a little negativity to doubt your thinking. It sometimes takes a lot of work and a lot of love for yourself to undo that damage."

"And that's why you gave me the tape?" Dana inquired.

"Bingo. If you're ready to change the old tape that's been playing in your head, I think my little tape will help you get started.

"Side A is a talk by one of my all-time favorite motivational speakers, one of many. He had a big influence on me and I think you'll find him very helpful. For this next week, I want you to listen to him for at least 15 minutes every day—yes?"

"Yes."

"Side B is all music. In the morning, when you get up, I want you to *really* get up! This is a collection of some of my favorite songs, the ones that always get me on my feet and remind me what I'm all about: *'I Feel Good,'* by James Brown, and *'R-E-S-P-E-C-T,'* by Aretha Franklin; *'My Way,'* by Old Blue Eyes himself, stuff like that. Later, you'll want to record your own favorite songs, but you can borrow mine for now. Honey, you listen to this every morning and it'll give you *go*-power like no breakfast cereal ever did!"

"Thank you." Dana said.

"Speaking of breakfast, have you eaten?" the Bag Lady inquired. "There are some delicious muffins in that basket."

"Oh, I'm too excited to eat this morning," declared Dana, suddenly realizing how strange those words felt in her mouth. Not hungry? She was always hungry!

"Skipping meals is no way to start a business, sweetheart. You're going to need lots of energy. Have a muffin—that's an order. And here, I have something else that will help keep you performing at peak efficiency all morning. Matter of fact, it's one of my company's products." The Bag Lady placed two capsules from a small plastic bottle into Dana's palm.

Dana was willing to try just about anything the Bag Lady suggested.

Meanwhile, her companion took a couple of the capsules herself, tossed down a large gulp of water. Dana quickly followed suit.

"What's in it?" she asked, trying to sound like she really cared about the ingredients.

"I honestly don't know, aside from the fact that it's all nutrients. Don't worry, it's really very good for you. I happen to know the scientists who formulated it and their work is very highly respected.

"Myself, I'm not a nutritionist. And I don't try to be. I just know what it does for me and what it's done for a lot of other people I care about. But you'll see. Just put it in your body and let me know how it feels about twenty minutes from now."

Dana quickly finished her water. "So tell me about this business of yours. How do we make money at it?"

"Believe it or not, you just completed step number one!" the Bag Lady answered, receiving a not-unexpected blank look in return.

"I'll explain later. Why don't I begin by telling you a little bit about how I happened to choose the company I joined."

It sounded to Dana as though it might be time to start taking notes, so she quickly reached for her purse. Meanwhile, the Bag Lady was once again digging into her own big black bag and soon retrieved a small plastic horse—the kind that often comes with those plastic toy farms made for toddlers. It was bright green with a purple mane. She held it up for Dana to admire.

"Hey," Dana remarked, "I think Katie has one something like that at home!"

"What can I tell you—once a teacher, always..." She handed the little horse to Dana. "I've known for quite awhile now that network marketing was an industry whose time was coming, that by the year 2000, who knows, even Ross Perot might be doing it.

"It didn't take me long to figure out that it offered me a chance to be both the breadwinner and the bread baker. With network marketing, it was possible for an ordinary housewife, working from her kitchen table, to earn more than the CEO of a Fortune 500 company. I got that loud and clear! But I made a few mistakes.

"Sometimes I listened to the wrong advice, instead of trusting my own intuition. You know that wonderful sacred energy we all have inside us?"

Dana nodded. "I see you're familiar with her," the Bag Lady replied.

"What I didn't realize was I needed to find a four-legged horse to ride if it was going to carry me all the way to the finish line a winner. I picked a few lame ones along the way, but I didn't give up—on network marketing or on myself. I mean you don't quit going to movies just because you wasted your money on one dud. You don't swear off men, because of one miserable date. I kept looking. And I finally figured out how to spot a thoroughbred.

"So, when I found this company, I made sure it met all my criteria—I made sure it had four strong legs under it."

The Bag Lady noticed Dana was still studying the horse as she listened.

"Write this down, Dear, it's important. I'm going to tell you what the four legs are." Dana picked up her pen.

"The first leg is *products*. Products are paramount. The product can be a tangible item you can hold in your hand, or it can be a service of some kind, but there has to be some real results-producing value that can be exchanged for money. Otherwise, there's no business. Now, here's where it gets tricky.

"You want a product that has integrity, that actually lives up to its promise. If it doesn't measure up to expectations, your customers won't come back and they certainly won't recommend it to their friends. Bad news travels fast. A product's poor reputation is likely to reflect on the company's credibility, too. You want to under-promise and over-deliver. That's the key to lasting success.

"Also, you don't want 'me-too' products. Those are ones that imitate what other companies are offering, or things that can be purchased at a store for the same price or less. And it's really great when you can offer world-class products that are backed by state-of-the-art knowledge, and, if you can throw in the names of well-known, highly-respected product developers, well, that's as good as it gets.

"I also look for consumable products, because then, if your product is really good, you've got happy customers for life. You don't have to keep finding new customers every month."

The Bag Lady spent the next several minutes describing her company's product line and explaining how they measured up to the requirements she had listed. After her brief overview, she paused and looked at Dana.

"How do you feel?" she asked Dana.

"Oh my head is swimming, there's so much to learn. It's really exciting!"

The Bag Lady smiled. "No, I mean, how do you *feel?* I believe it's been about thirty minutes now since we had our "vitamins...."

Dana thought for a moment. She felt very alive, very awake, like a greasy film had been wiped off the windshield of her mind. In short, she felt great!

"Hey! You know, I feel ready to take on the world! I know I was already pretty charged up when I got here, but there's gotta be more going on here—this is incredible! Could it really be just the vitamins?"

"You tell me. Personally, I call it peak performance and personal power in a pill."

"Wow," Dana commented. "You know, this stuff could save some marriages! I've got a friend who needs this in the worst way. I can't wait to tell her."

"Bingo! Did you hear what you just said...? You said 'I can't wait to tell her!' Now you're on your way to a fortune!"

"I'm not sure I follow."

"You've just discovered something you wanted to tell your friend about. It didn't have a thing to do with selling anything. It was about sharing something great with her, because she's your friend and you know it'll help her. But guess what, you *are* going to make money regardless, every time you turn somebody on. And what do you think might happen when your friends try it—maybe they won't be able to shut up about it either. Do you see what could happen?"

"Wow!" Dana exclaimed. "Hey, you know, I was just thinking. Didn't you say there was a product for weight-loss, too?"

"You bet there is."

"Well, if it works half as well as that energy stuff, I want to try it right away. Nothing else has worked for me, so what have I got to lose—except maybe 50 pounds?"

The Bag Lady was rummaging in her bag again. This time she emerged with an enlarged snapshot in a vinyl page protector. "It worked for me," she said, "and I had been losing the diet war for decades. This is my "before picture."

"You're kidding!"

"I'm not kidding."

"You're not kidding?"

"I told you, products with integrity."

An immense grin overtook Dana's face. "I'm going to be rich!" She was laughing now.

"How about *thin* and rich?" the Bag Lady suggested as she joined in laughing.

In a little while they were back to business.

"Before we go on to the other three legs of the horse," Dana asked, "do you think you could just tell me what to say to my friend, Jenna, about the products? I want to call her tonight,"

"I can do better than that," the Bag Lady said. "Do you know how to reach your friend during the day?"

"Sure, I have her work number."

"Why don't we call her now and I'll help you tell her about it."

"Really! That'd be great! Where's the phone...oh, it's right here." Dana was flustered, but eager to place her first business call. But in mid-dial she stopped, frozen.

"Wait, what should I say? I want to be sure to get this right."

Together, the Bag Lady and Dana practiced a simple opening statement that sounded natural for Dana and would let her friend know right up front how excited she was about the new product she had just tried and how great it made her feel. If Jenna had time to talk briefly and showed any interest in hearing about it at all, Dana would explain that she didn't know all the answers yet, but her new friend and business partner was right there to explain.

It was nothing but the truth. Dana dialed, talked—and, it worked. On the strength of Dana's conviction, Jenna was willing to give the product a try, even before she knew about the 30-day, money-back guarantee. And she wanted to hear more about the weight loss product, too. Dana handed the phone over to the Bag Lady, who warmly introduced herself, then moved quickly into her story.

"So, Jenna, our friend Dana insists that I tell you about the 60 pounds I lost…"

Within 30 seconds, Jenna learned that the mysterious woman on the other end of the line had been skeptical at first, but desperate enough to try anything, that she was amazed and excited by her results and that she felt absolutely great.

"And Jenna, the best part is, I lost the weight without dieting!" the Bag Lady crooned.

Jenna could scarcely believe her ears. She started to ask questions about the ingredients, but the Bag Lady gently cut her short.

"Jenna, I have no idea how it works. I leave that to the biochemists who developed it. They're obviously pretty brilliant. I just know that it works and that I've never felt healthier. But you don't have to take anybody's word for it. It's 100% guaranteed. You get all your money back if it doesn't work, so there's really nothing to lose, right? Let me tell you about my friend Tracey who lost 100 pounds…and my neighbor, Dennis who…"

Jenna eagerly agreed to try the program based on those exciting testimonies.

Dana made arrangements to drop off the order at Jenna's house the next morning before she left for her afternoon shift. She was euphoric. Her first sale!

But wait—how was she going to sell products when she didn't have any herself? The Bag Lady came to the rescue.

"You're absolutely right, Honey, it's tough to sell out of an empty wagon. You're definitely going to want to have products on hand if you want your business to go fast. But since you've got a real live customer waiting and I just happen to have what you need, I'll help you get started. We'll sell my products to your customer, split the profit, and you can use your proceeds to start investing in your own inventory. Fair enough?"

"More than fair!" Dana couldn't believe the way her new mentor was looking after her interests. She'd never had bosses who cared about anything but covering their backsides and protecting the company's bottom line.

"Don't worry, you won't need a huge stockpile of products. Once you get your new customers started properly, you can show them how to order for themselves, directly from the company, and your retail profits will be mailed to you by check. But for the moment, I'd like us to concentrate on putting some right-now cash money in your pocket. I know that's important to you."

"You don't know how important!"

"I don't know?...Hey Dana, this is me, remember? The lady who used to get to the checkout counter at the supermarket and have to put items back after the cashier rang up the sale. The lady who couldn't afford to buy the large economy size of diapers. Trust me, I know."

The Bag Lady made a mental note to order some products and have them express shipped to her—it looked like she and Dana were going to be busy for a few days.

"Now, let's get back to that four-legged horse. I know you can relate to this next one—it's called *profit potential*."

"Yeah, that sounds important all right," Dana chimed in. "But how would I know about something like that? I mean, I'm no financial wizard. I'm lucky if my checkbook balances."

"Well, that might be something you want to work on— later—but that has nothing to do with profit potential," the Bag Lady said. "What I mean is simply this: can you make money at it? You might have the best, most unique products in the world, but if hardly anybody has a need for them, how are you going to make any money...?

"You need to think about who's going to buy your products, how big is the market—really?

"Remember how quickly you were able to think of someone else who needed extra energy after you experienced what that product did for you? Now that's a big market—am I right?

"Okay, the other half of profit potential is the company's compensation structure," the Bag Lady continued. "The issue here is how much you can earn for your efforts."

"Each multi-level company has its own pay plan, which determines how much you make on your own retail sales, and how much you earn when you teach other people to do what you do.

"What you want is a company that sets its distributors up to win, because that company is still going to be sending you royalty checks, God willing, for years to come. You want a company that lets you earn a healthy profit on every consumer sale you make—I call that right-now money.

"But you also want to be able to earn good money on the distributor organization you build, because that's what's going to pay for Katie's and Kevin's college. That's where your mortgage installment and your car payments are going to come from, even after you decide to retire. We call that long-term royalty income. It's a wonderful thing!"

"Wait a minute," an incredulous Dana exclaimed. "Are you saying I can make money even when I'm not working? That sounds too good to be true!"

"I know," the Bag Lady said shaking her head, "and I haven't even told you just *how* good. That's probably the single greatest barrier I have to overcome in building my business. People just can't believe the power of it. Most people are so programmed to live within all kinds of limits: Limits on what they're allowed to do, where they can go, how much they can eat or drink, how high they can rise in their career, how much they can get paid...

"But in this business, there are no limits on what you can earn. It's just amazing how uncomfortable some people get when you take their limits away."

"I think I know what you mean," Dana said thoughtfully. "When I was married, my husband was very controlling. He told me what to wear, how much I could spend on the groceries, who I was allowed to be friends with. I even had to get his permission to go anywhere without him. Can you believe that? But after he left me, it felt so weird. It was actually kind of scary. I guess I wasn't used to the freedom...."

"Or the responsibility," the Bag Lady observed. "When your ex was around, you had someone else to blame for whatever was wrong in your life. Freedom means you have to take responsibility for yourself. Believe it or not, that's not what everybody wants."

"Well, I sure do!" Dana stated resolutely. "No more limits for me!"

"Now you're talking like a winner!"

The Bag Lady continued with a simplified explanation of her company's compensation plan, while Dana scribbled furiously in her notebook. Her mentor drew diagrams on a sheet of paper. It all seemed complex, technical at first but the Bag Lady explained in plain and simple English, avoiding terms she knew would be strange to Dana.

After a broad overview, she translated the key principles into dollars and cents with some easy examples. She finished by focusing on a few simple, attainable, short-term goals for Dana—her teaching skills coming in handy.

She could see Dana had absorbed about as much new information as she could handle at one time. The Bag Lady had learned long ago not to overload new people with too much all at once. It was time to end the first lesson.

"Oh, look at the time!" the Bag Lady exclaimed. "I've got to get to Queens by noon. I'm meeting my aunt for lunch. We'll continue this tomorrow. Here's what I want you to do 'til then.

"Take a sheet of paper and draw a line down the middle. On the left side, I want you to make a list of everybody you know who lives within driving distance. I'll bet you'll even need more than one sheet of paper for this," she said. Being a good gardener, she was always planting seeds of positive expectation. "Don't leave anybody out: hairdresser, mail carrier, bank teller—everybody you know by face or name.

"On the right side, I want you to list everybody you know who lives outside the area: Former classmates, distant cousins, whatever. Don't think, just write. I'll explain tomorrow."

They made plans to meet at 9:00 A.M. the next day.

Dana's brain was in high gear as she walked out of the hotel. Park Avenue was awash in sunshine. Across the street, Central Park was a lush, vivid picture postcard photo opportunity. The forsythia frothed fountains of yellow over the sidewalks. The city looked completely different from the dim, drizzly streets she'd trudged through on her fruitless job search just a day ago. She felt like walking all 15 blocks to the Port Authority and headed downtown with a light, yet determined stride.

It was amazing, she thought, how different everything seemed today. Just as the changeable spring weather had transformed the city streets from one day to the next, the climate in her head and heart had warmed considerably.

As she walked, Dana remembered what the Bag Lady had said about "changing the tape" in her head, and realized it must be happening already. She was feeling so good about her decision to reach out and grab this new opportunity.

Just then, she noticed a bookstore across the street. It had been a long time since she'd set foot inside one of those. Well, it was time to start loading up her mind with good things, like the Bag Lady said.

She crossed at the corner and went inside. She automatically gravitated to the second-hand book section at the back of the store and started sorting through the stacks of books. A title caught her eye and she picked the book up.

The Way to Happiness was the title. The cover was in good condition. The book had obviously been handled lovingly and opened often. The author, Bishop Fulton J. Sheen, was unfamiliar to Dana. As she flipped casually through the pages, the book seemed to open itself to one well-worn page. The first few lines jumped off the page at her:

> "Each of us makes our own weather,
>   determines the color of the skies
>   in the emotional universe which they
>   alone inhabit."

That night, when the Bag Lady returned to her hotel room after a very productive dinner meeting, the message light on her phone was blinking. Dana had called at 7:35 P.M. The Bag Lady dialed her number as she slipped out of her shoes.

"Miss me already, Honey?" she quipped when Dana answered.

"Oh, I'm so glad you called back! This is so exciting. I was talking to my friend, Linda. And she said I sounded so perky and wanted to know what was up. And so I told her about the energy product, and she asked where can she get some. So, I started telling her about you and what we've been doing. And guess what...?"

"She wants to know more about it?"

"Better than that! She wants to know if she can sell it, too! Isn't that great?" Dana's voice was bursting with excitement and before her new friend could answer, she chattered on.

"And then, a few minutes later, my friend Susan, who is also a friend of Linda's, called and said she'd just gotten off the phone with Linda, and she wanted to know if she could come over, too, when I explain it all to Linda!"

"So, here's what I was thinking." Dana was clearly on a roll. "Since you're already delivering the products for Jenna tomorrow morning, maybe you could also sit down and talk with Linda and Susan while you're out this way. It's like magic, isn't it? Oh please, say yes!"

What Dana couldn't see was the delighted smile at the other end of the line.

"Yes!" the Bag Lady answered.

"Now listen, Dana. Can you see what's happening here? You've already got your first wave going. So, let's ride it all the way in. Get on the phone tonight and tomorrow morning and talk to some more of your friends, just exactly the way you talked to Linda and Susan. When they sound interested, tell them to come over tomorrow for your party and they can hear all about it there. Get as many people as you can fit into your apartment and I'll show you some *real* magic."

A little while later, she said good night to Dana. Hanging up the receiver, she felt an old familiar satisfaction that never failed to please her, no matter how many times she trained a new distributor.

"Yesssss," she whispered, and then out loud, "I *love* this business!" And she did a little dance.

CHAPTER FOUR
The Party: Playing for Profit

The next morning went by very quickly. Dana, using good common sense, convinced Jenna to come over to her apartment for the party, instead of delivering the product to her. Dana figured the Bag Lady's valuable time would be better spent if she could talk to everyone at once. She wanted as much of her mentor's knowledge as she could possibly get. Time was money, she laughed.

After a quick, early morning phone conversation with the Bag Lady, Dana knew exactly what to do to get ready for her party. Nothing. Well, almost nothing. She had enough chairs for everyone, but that wasn't important, the Bag Lady had told her.

She had a TV with a VCR, ready to play the video her mentor was bringing, which was also nice to have, but also not necessary.

She had to be forgetting something, she thought. This was much too easy. The Bag Lady arrived 30 minutes before her friends were expected.

"Today you're going to start earning your crown! You're on your way to royalty!" the Bag Lady said as Dana opened the front door. She breezed in carrying her customary big black bag over one shoulder, plus a second, much larger nylon bag, obviously well packed and ready for business, over her other shoulder.

Dana helped her move the kitchen table into the living room, close to the television.

Then the Bag Lady opened the larger brightly colored bag and began setting up a simple product display on the table. Meanwhile Dana set up her boom box and started the cassette of favorite "power songs" the Bag Lady had given her. Before long they were both snapping their fingers and moving in time to the music as they set up. Within five minutes, everything was ready. Dana was vibrating with anticipation.

"So, what was this magic you mentioned on the phone last night?" Dana asked.

"I'm so glad you asked, Honey! Here's the deal. The magic is today. What you make of this day will determine the future of your business. It's going to provide the raw material you're going to use to create your financial destiny. It's pure alchemy. Do you have any idea what I'm talking about?"

"No. Not really."

"This business you're building is based on a little notion called duplication. To get that long-term royalty income we talked about—which is where the real gold is hidden—you're going to teach people to do what you do, and then teach them to teach others, and then they're going to teach more people, and so on and so on.

"So, the key is, whether the master copy is worth duplicating. And guess who the master copy is?"

Dana's face lit up with sudden comprehension. "Me!"

"Bingo! And because you are the master copy, your first 48 hours will create the model that your entire organization is going to follow. So, think about that.

"Do you see how important right now is—it's the first hour of your 48 Hour Plan And if that doesn't catch your hair on fire right now, watch what happens when your friends get here. Magic."

Just then, the doorbell rang. Dana jumped up and literally ran to answer it. Within minutes, five of her friends were assembled in the living room, enjoying themselves and chatting. Dana excused herself for a moment and went into the kitchen to consult the Bag Lady.

"Oh, I'm so disappointed. Two of my friends didn't show up. Sherry just called with some dumb excuse. I don't even know what happened to Lisa."

"Relax, Dana. Forget about who's not here. Just focus on who *is* here. You're about to offer each of them one of the greatest gifts of their lives. C'mon. Show time."

This was the part of the business the Bag Lady loved most—meeting new people. She never got tired of it. She was truly a people person, and she loved being the entertainer, too. Dana introduced her to each of her friends and the Bag Lady chatted warmly with each of them for a moment. Then, she effortlessly began her presentation.

"I'm so excited to have this chance to meet all of you and tell you about something that has absolutely transformed my life. You know, I didn't always look like this. Just a few years ago I weighed over 250 pounds and I was $250,000 in debt." She grinned impishly. "Tell me, is that symmetrical or what?

"I'm actually very serious...I was really, really desperate. That's what's so great about my story. I didn't just start with nothing, I started with *less than* less than nothing..." And the Bag Lady launched into her rags-to-riches story, the very same one she'd told Dana in the cab, the very same story she'd told again and again and again in the course of her business. She never tired of telling it—it was her truth. And it carried a very powerful message.

When she'd finished, she asked Dana to tell about her brief experience with the company's products and then she introduced a short video that would explain what was happening for people all over the country. Dana walked over to the VCR and, with a sweeping gesture and a smile, pushed "Play."

The video contained some basic information about the company along with dozens of quick, dramatic testimonies by ordinary-seeming people who had gotten great results using the products. Many of these people described how their enjoyment of the products had led to a great business opportunity, and how their lives had changed as a result.

When the video ended, it was apparent that some of Dana's friends found it quite inspiring. One, however, sat with her arms tightly folded and her jaw set tight. The Bag Lady correctly guessed she'd walked in with her negative attitude already in place, since she had seated herself in the chair nearest the door. The Bag Lady responded by inclining her body more toward the other women in the room.

"So, you can see the products work. And, by the way, they all come with a 100% money-back guarantee. Of course, with products that work this well, there's also obviously a great business opportunity for anyone who's interested in making money. So, what I want to know is, who's interested in results like the ones you just heard about and who's interested in becoming financially free?"

There was the briefest of silences. The Bag Lady didn't have to wait long for a response.

Susan couldn't wait to find out how to lose weight.

Linda was interested in the business.

Jenna, of course, had walked in expecting to buy and get a sample of the weight loss product, too. But based on what she'd just heard, she was ready to skip the sample and buy the whole package!

All three women seemed much more animated than when they'd walked in. The power of the products, the Bag Lady thought.

She asked Linda if she'd mind waiting a few moments, while she first filled product orders for Susan and Jenna. Then she asked Jenna and Susan several questions, so that she could design the right program for each of them. She chatted amiably while bagging up their purchases.

"I know Dana is as excited as I am that you're both going to do this. Once you start seeing results, we're going to show you how to get your product for free, and maybe even put a few extra dollars in your pocket besides. Then, later on, if you're interested, we can show you how to make anywhere from $500 to $5,000 a month, or even more, like I do. But only if you want to. If not, you have to promise me that when all your friends and relatives start asking you what you're doing—and I promise you, they will—you'll send them to Dana, because we build this business on referrals. Deal?"

"Believe me," countered Jenna, "if this weight comes off me after everything I've tried, even my husband will try it, and he's one of the world's all time skeptics."

"And that's exactly what we're going to focus on for now—getting you results. But I do have to warn you about something." The Bag Lady winked. "Do you remember hearing about the famous Klopnick Diamond? You know, it was this spectacular 10 carat diamond that had a curse that came with it...The curse was Mr. Klopnick! This program is like that. It doesn't come with a curse, it comes with a coach, and that coach is me.

"I'm going to stick with you on this program 'til we start seeing those pounds and inches falling off. So, you need to tell me now what's the best time to call you and at what number—Okay?" The two women readily agreed.

Now, the Bag Lady turned her attention to Linda, who had also brought her friend Eve to the party.

"So, Linda, Dahling, tell me, did you see us doing anything today that you wouldn't feel comfortable doing yourself?" the Bag Lady asked.

"No. But I'm sure there's more to it, isn't there?" asked Linda.

"It's actually a very simple business. There are lots of ways to go about it, depending on your own personal style. And there are lots of tools the company provides to make it easy for you. The main issue you need to consider is; number one, what do you want to get out of it? And number two, how much time are you willing to spend to get it?

"Have you thought about that?"

Linda pondered for a moment. "Well, I don't know if this is realistic or not, but I just hate my job. My boss is a total jerk, the work is boring and there's really no future in it for me. I mean, I'd just love to quit the whole scene like my sister and brother-in-law. They have their own business; they work from home and they make their own rules. That really appeals to me. I've wanted to have a business of my own for the longest time, but I don't have any money to start one. Do you really think I could make a living at this?"

"That really depends on you, dear. I've trained quite a few people who live very, very well on this business. Others in my organization prefer to do it part-time for the supplementary income they get or to build up long-term royalty income for the future. It's a very personal choice," the Bag Lady answered.

"What I want know from you is the same thing I asked Dana yesterday: Are you teachable? Are you committed?"

"I just know I could do this, but you know, I'd like to talk it over with my husband. I want him to support me on this decision," said Linda.

"That's a good idea. We can talk some more tomorrow after you've had time to really give it some serious thought," the Bag Lady assured her.

"In the meantime," Linda said, "I'd like to get started on some of those products you talked about. And could you tell me more about the vitamins? I think I'm going to take some home for my mom and my sister and, of course, my kids should be on them—right? And what about that stuff that helps people sleep better?"

By the time they finished talking, Linda had ordered over $100 worth of products and Eve had gotten samples to try.

"Listen, Linda, whether or not you decide to do the business, I think we'd better get you signed up as a preferred customer, so you can buy all this stuff at a discount. You'll come out way ahead that way," the Bag Lady suggested.

Linda agreed. As soon as she had completed her application and paid for her products, the Bag Lady turned to Dana and started counting out $20 bills.

"Here, Dana, this is your share of the profits for today." She handed Dana $80. It was hard to tell whose eyes got bigger, Dana's or Linda's...

"I was just thinking," Linda said. "What if I invited a bunch of people over to my house like you guys did today?

Would I make money like that, too? Because I bet my husband would be a lot more positive about all this if he saw you hand *me* money like you just gave Dana."

"Now, you're thinking like a winner!" the Bag Lady applauded. "I have tomorrow evening available. Can you make it happen by then?"

"I'll try," she answered.

"Lesson Number One, Linda. Get rid of that word. Wipe it out of your vocabulary right now."

"Here,' the Bag Lady said to Linda, placing her Mont Blanc on the coffee table, *"Try* to pick up that pen."

Linda just looked at her.

"Go ahead, *try...* "

Linda began to smile.

"Ahhh. You got it," the Bag Lady smiled with her. "There is no *try,* Linda. Have you seen *Star Wars?* Remember Yoda, the Jedi Master? He told Luke Skywalker, 'Do, or do not, Luke. There is no try.' So, do or do not, Linda. Can you make it happen by then?"

"Right. I'll *do* it!" said Linda, with head-nodding conviction.

Linda bounced out with her products under her arm and a big smile on her face. Dana had a smile dancing across her face, as well.

What a way to make a living, the Bag Lady thought. Making people feel good. Helping them get what they want in their lives.

"I *love* this business!" she shouted—and she did her little dance right there in Dana's kitchen.

They talked for another half hour or so about the business and the Bag Lady continued her explanation of the four-legged horse she'd been telling Dana about the day before. The third leg she looked for in selecting a solid opportunity, she said, was *leadership.*

"It's very important to have company leaders who know what it takes to build an outstanding MLM company, and how to make their distributors successful. It doesn't matter whether they're famous sports figures or business tycoons, or even important scientists—they need to know network marketing. Let's face it, Dahling, Cher may know how to achieve tight buns, but I'm not sure I'd want her running my company."

"Squeaky clean is a quality I also look for in leaders." the Bag Lady continued. "You want a company that's going to survive any kind of legal scrutiny. One which will last a long, long time. Leaders who have integrity are going to build a company that has integrity. And vice versa," she added.

"The fourth leg is the *Support System*. The better the support system, the easier it is for us to build our business. The more of your work the company is able to take over, the more time you can spend retailing and recruiting and developing your new distributors. You'll see how important that is as we work together over the next few weeks."

"That sure makes sense. It's kind of like having a house-keeper, right? Leaves more time for Mommy to be a mommy?" Dana asked.

"Exactly. Now, how's that list coming along, the one with the names of everyone you know?"

Dana dug out a lined tablet from the kitchen drawer. "Here's what I've got so far. I guess I really don't know that many people." The paper had about 20 names on the left side and six names on the right.

"We can work with this for today, but I know there are lots more people you haven't remembered. Did you know the average person knows about 300 people by name?"

"That seems incredible." Dana frowned.

"Do you save Christmas cards?" the Bag Lady asked.

"Every card I ever got, probably."

"I thought so. Get them out. Also, do you still have your school yearbooks?" Dana was nodding. "And go through your Yellow Pages, too. Look at each category, like architect, attorney, baker, butcher, and ask yourself, 'who do I know in that line of work? Who's my favorite cleaner? Who runs my neighborhood food store?' And so forth. You can do that this evening."

"What we're going to do right now, is work with the list you have so far."

Using a brief phone introduction the Bag Lady had suggested, Dana called each person on the left side of the list, and then turned the phone over to her friend. The Bag Lady briefly explained the reason for their call, that she and Dana were new business partners, and that they were introducing a revolutionary line of nutritional products to the area. She very quickly described the kinds of results people were getting, including her own.

She politely asked each person if they'd be kind enough to listen to a brief call and check out the company website and give her their opinion of them. By the time they got to the bottom of the list, they'd only caught six people in, and they left messages for the others.

Of the six they actually spoke with, there were four who were willing to get the call that evening, and she made appointments with each of them. They scheduled the other two for different time slots that week.

Next, they tackled the list on the right side of the page. They reached two of these people and used a similar approach to have them agree to view the tape. Both were willing, and the Bag Lady agreed to send them a package by Priority Mail the next day. Both of them were also interested in trying a sample of the products, which would be included in the package.

"Well, Dana, I'd say we're having a pretty productive day so far. I think it's time we started keeping score." The Bag Lady produced a sheet of paper from her big bag. It had a large grid drawn on it with words like, "Presentations" and "Home parties" printed to the left of each horizontal line. The days of the week were printed at the top of each vertical column.

"This is where you record your 'figs and guages.' 'Figs' is short for the word 'figures' and 'gauges' are measurements. Each day, you measure what you accomplished in comparison to the other days. It gives you a instant snapshot of how your business is going." The Bag Lady helped Dana fill in her figures so far.

"And the day's not nearly over yet!" Dana added proudly.

"I like the way you think, Honey" the Bag Lady agreed. "I have some other business to take care of today, and I know Katie will be home from school any minute now. Why don't I come back around six o'clock for our appointments this evening?"

"If you hear from any of the people we left messages with, do you think you'll know what to say?" the Bag Lady asked.

"I...think so." Dana sounded a little doubtful.

"You decide how to handle them. If you feel comfortable talking with the people on your own, go for it. If you need help, just find out the best time to catch them at home and later on we'll call them together. Okay?"

Dana brightened. Somehow it made her feel a little more confident knowing her friend would be around to back her up.

"Yes. Okay," she agreed.

"I'll just leave you with this. Maybe it'll help you remember what all of this is about." The Bag Lady pulled something out of her bag and handed it to Dana. It was a little hand spade, the kind a gardener might use to loosen the soil in a flower pot.

"There's an old saying, Dana. 'You can count how many seeds there are in an apple, but you can never know how many apples there are in a seed.' Think of your business as planting seeds, Dana. That's exactly what we've been doing today. And even if only a few of those seeds sprout, once they've taken root, they have the ability to grow into marvelous trees, which multiply on their own.

"It's our job to tend them; water them, keep the soil rich and help in every way we can, but they have their own strength within them. When they're ready, they'll know how to duplicate themselves."

"You know," Dana thought out loud, "even my ex had to give me credit for having a green thumb. Maybe it'll work for me in my business."

The Bag Lady continued. "I sometimes see people who attack their businesses like hunters stalking prey. It makes me sad, because I know it's not going to last. A hunter might have the ability to bag a lot of game in a single day, but the next day he's on to the next safari. Meanwhile, today's catch is stuck away in a freezer or it's mounted on some wall. It's dead. Nothing can grow from it.

"So, you know what to do—just keep sowing lots and lots of seeds. And the second you see that little speck of green poking through the dirt, it's time to go to work!"

As the Bag Lady opened the apartment door to leave, Katie was rushing up the hall, flushed with excitement. She was still in high spirits from her school day. It was wonderful, Dana mused, how much her children loved learning. They soaked up new experiences like little sponges. It seemed like a shame the way most people, at some point in life, started resisting and began to look upon learning as work.

Dana said good-bye to the Bag Lady and turned to smile at Katie as she closed the door behind her.

"Good day, sweetie?" she asked.

Katie had already dug a masterpiece from her book bag and was beaming with pride as she held it up for her mother to admire.

"Look, Mommy! I made a mask today, like the people in Africa!"

The mask was an oval of corrugated cardboard, punched with two eye holes. Katie had glued on beans dyed with food coloring, kernels of corn and a variety of seeds and grasses in a bright, bold design. Ceremoniously, Dana attached it to the refrigerator door with magnets.

"Mommy, can I watch the Care Bears video while I have my snack?"

"I guess so, honey. Just for a little while, okay?" Dana opened the cabinet in the TV stand and rummaged through the tapes. As usual, they were in total disarray and she had to sort through them to read the labels. As she did so, Katie knelt down on the floor next to her.

"What's this for, Mommy?" Dana glanced at Katie, who had picked up the garden spade the Bag Lady had left.

"It's a tool for gardening, Katie. You use it to dig with, so you can plant seeds."

"Are we going to make a garden, Mommy? Can we grow a flower?"

Dana looked at her daughter and smiled.

"I already have a flower growing in my garden, baby. You're my perfect little flower." And she playfully grabbed Katie, who pretended to struggle as her mother planted a giant smooch on her forehead. In the tussle, a videotape slid out of the cabinet and landed on the floor next to Dana. She picked it up and looked at the label. It read:

"Field of Dreams"

CHAPTER FIVE

Some Will: Some Won't

The phone rang as Dana was adding water to the Hamburger Helper mix. She lowered the flame under the skillet and dashed to answer it on the third ring.

It was Lonnie Andrews, a former next door neighbor from when she was married. Lonnie was on Dana's list and had received a message to call back earlier in the day when Dana had been making calls with the Bag Lady.

"Dana, I haven't heard from you in ages! What's new with you? How are the kids?"

Dana was genuinely delighted to hear her old friend's voice. It had been much too long. "The kids are great, Lonnie. How 'bout yours? Stephie must be in third grade by now, right?"

"Good memory! She's just fine. And I guess you haven't heard my latest news, have you?" Lonnie couldn't wait for Dana to guess that she was pregnant again.

They spent a few minutes catching up on each others' lives as Dana waited anxiously for the opening so she could explain the reason for her call. She really liked Lonnie—she'd forgotten how much—and she couldn't wait to share her news with her friend.

"Lonnie, I've got some news, too! That's why I called. Are you ready?"

"Tell me! You've got a new boyfriend. You're getting married! What...?"

"Nope. None of the above. I've started a business!"

"No way! That's so great, Dana! Tell me about it. What is it?"

And Dana went for it.

She explained what was going on briefly, just as she'd practiced with the Bag Lady. She asked Lonnie if she had time to look at the tape that evening and Lonnie was more than accommodating. They set a time for later. The whole thing went perfectly. She couldn't wait to tell the Bag Lady.

"Yessss!" She whispered to herself as she returned to the stove. She turned the burner back up and lifted the lid. And, as she stirred the contents of the skillet, she caught herself doing a variation of the Bag Lady's little dance.

Katie had finished her dinner and Dana was just removing Kevin from the highchair when the phone rang again. This time, Dana was filled with self assurance as she picked up the receiver.

"Dana, it's me. I got a message that you called earlier. What's up?"

It was Aaron, her brother. Piece of cake, she thought. Dana launched into her routine.

From the very beginning of the conversation, though, it just didn't go according to plan.

"Look, Dana. I don't see how you can even think about starting some wacky business right now. You're the one person I know who's more broke than I am. And what do you know about business, anyway? You need a job, baby sister. Don't you get it?"

"And just who's going to hire me, Aaron? I've been all over town!" Dana could feel her voice rising in her throat. This isn't what she wanted to talk about! She fought to regain her composure.

"Aaron, listen. This is better than a job. This is a future. I can be my own boss, work from home and be with my kids. I know I can do this! I have this wonderful woman training me, and she's a millionaire, Aaron. She's showing me how to do just what she did!"

"Aw, for cryin' out loud, Dana! Don't tell me you bought that line! You believe that crap she's giving you! Listen, even if she did know how to make that kind of money, why would she tell you? She's not crazy!"

Dana felt a familiar stinging in her eyes. She was 13 years old again, hearing her big brother put down her latest heart throb. She felt stupid. Frustrated. She was silent for a moment, struggling to find her next words.

Aaron continued in a patronizing tone. "Look, Dana, I don't want to be the one to rain on your parade, but let's face it. Doesn't all this sound just a little too good to be true? I've been suckered into enough scams myself to know one when I see one. I'm just trying to look out for my baby sister, ya know."

Dana finally found her voice.

"You know, Aaron, when I thought about starting a business, you were the first person I thought of to be my partner. I thought we could have a family business, together, just like we used to talk about when we were kids. Like the Dalucci's down the street, remember?

"But I guess I made a mistake. Partners have to trust and respect each other. You obviously don't trust or respect me. So, I don't think we have any more to talk about." She hung up the receiver hard.

Her lip was trembling. She wanted to scream. How could her own brother be such a jerk! The one person she thought she could count on to always support her. The guy she'd bailed out of one jam after another over the years, who even now owed her $200! How could he be so condescending?

The door bell rang. She looked at the clock and realized it was time for the Bag Lady to return. Darn! She didn't want anyone to see her like this, especially her new friend.

She rubbed her eyes to stuff the tears back in, crossed the apartment to answer the door, checking the hall mirror for smeared mascara as she passed. But when she opened the door, her weak smile didn't fool the Bag Lady for a moment.

"Let me guess, Honey" said the Bag Lady as she came in. "I'd say you've just had a close encounter of the terrible kind. So, who was the dream stealer?"

Dana sighed and went limp. There was no point in holding back the tears now.

"Here," said the Bag Lady, handing her a tissue. "Can we talk?"

The words spilled out all in a rush. Dana's five-minute conversation with her brother—now hopelessly entangled with their entire history together—unraveled like a giant ball of saved string. The Bag Lady listened silently, patiently.

"Are you finished?" she asked when Dana finally fell silent. She received a puzzled look from Dana in reply.

"And more to the point, what is it that you're finished with? If you can be finished with the conversation you just had with your brother and put it behind you once and for all, great. If you can't be finished with that business, then I'd say you're finished with this business. So, time to make a decision, Honey."

"I don't want to quit!" Dana said assertively. "I just had this crazy idea that for once in my life things could work out between my brother and me. I thought I'd finally found something we could share."

"And be a real family—like on TV, right? Everybody's nice 'n' sweet to each other and all their challenges get happily resolved and everything ends pleasantly in 27 minutes and you run out and buy all the products on the ads?" the Bag Lady gently teased.

"I've got a great name for your new TV show—we'll call it 'Poor Pitiful Pearl.' You can be the star!"

Dana managed a flicker of a smile. She sniffed as she mopped at her eyes with the tissue.

"You know, over the years, I've watched how a lot of people operate. It seems to me there are basically two types: Whiners and Winners. All that separates them is the letter 'h.' And it seems to me that 'h' stands for 'history.' So, what do you say we have ourselves a quick history lesson?"

"Okay," Dana agreed, sniffling and smiling.

"So, Dahling, let's talk about you and your brother. I guess you've always really looked up to him, right?

"Yes."

"You've always really worked for his approval?"

Dana wasn't sure why this line of questioning made her uncomfortable. She wore a confused look. "Well, yeah, I guess so."

"So, I can assume," the Bag Lady continued in earnest, "he's been much more successful in life than you have been?"

"Actually, he's still searching for the right career. He's tried a lot of different things, but nothing ever seems to work out quite right," Dana answered.

"Oh, you're saying he demands a lot of himself. His standards of excellence are very high?"

"I don't know about that. The same as most I suppose."

"You mean mediocre? But, surely there's one particular area where he really stands out though, right?" the Bag Lady continued her questioning.

"Umm, well not really anything I can think of..." Dana was screwing up her face with concentration. She was beginning to catch the Bag Lady's drift.

"But what about his friends. A person with wonderful, loyal friends is a very wealthy person indeed. That's probably your brother's strong suit, right?"

"I can't stand his friends. They're kinda mean—and a pretty shiftless bunch, too, if you ask me. They'd probably dump him for a buck." The light was dawning on Dana's face.

"Oh. I see. So, what about courage? They say without courage, all other virtues are useless. If that brother of yours is anything like his sister, I'll bet he's probably got guts. He's always willing to take risks in life—right?"

Dana stared the Bag Lady straight in the eye. It was all very clear now.

"You mean like starting this business with me? I think I've got your point. No, he wasn't willing to take the chance. He thinks everything's some kind of scam."

"Oh, I see." The Bag Lady shot Dana a knowing look over the top of her reading glasses.

"So, let's review the facts. I'm sure you love your brother very much and nothing should ever change that. No discussion on that point.

"However, you did just tell me that your brother doesn't know what he wants to do with his life, hasn't ever been very good or very successful at anything, has no money, no real friends—and, no guts. Now, maybe you can tell me, how he's qualified to tell you whether or not you're making a good decision about anything?"

Dana opened her mouth to answer, but no words came.

"And furthermore, Dana, why should it trouble you that he doesn't want to be your business partner? He doesn't sound like very good partner material to me!"

"I see your point," Dana conceded, a little sadly.

"I'm not here to judge your brother, Dana. Whatever your history together, whatever factors brought the two of you to this point in your lives, you both could use a break. And you both have an equal opportunity.

"You chose to go for it. He chose not to—for now.

"For now. That's important for you to remember, Dana. When somebody says 'No,' it doesn't always mean 'No,' and it certainly doesn't mean 'No,' forever! Sometimes it just means 'I don't get it. I need more information.'

"Sometimes it means you just caught them at the wrong moment and their minds will be more open, or their needs will be more apparent, at some other time.

"And sometimes—like maybe with your brother—it just so happens that he doesn't have quite as much hope, or quite as much vision, or quite as much courage, as you do. And maybe he needs you to go first. Maybe he needs you to show him that it really can be done. Light the way, you know? We all need that from somebody, some time in our lives."

Dana smiled warmly, confidently. She was feeling a lot better about things now.

"So, c'mon, Dahling" the Bag Lady prodded. "Go put on a new face, while I see what you've got in your closet to wear this evening. I want you looking and feeling like a winner! You know what they say—you gotta dress up and make up to go up!"

Dana laughed and headed into the bathroom with a little dance.

A half hour later, the sitter was reading a story to Katie, baby Kevin was nodding off to sleep in his crib, and Dana was on her way out the door with the Bag Lady. They had a busy evening ahead. Four presentations!

"You were right about getting dressed up," Dana confided. "I feel so much better. In fact, you've been right about everything! From now on I'm not going to let anybody pull me down."

"Is that a commitment?" the Bag Lady challenged.

"You bet it is!"

"You can't be sometimes-committed, you know. Commitment is a 24-seven deal."

"I'm in. Just do it!" Dana declared.

A satisfied smile came over the Bag Lady's face.

"I know a little story about commitment. Did you ever hear about George and Martha playing golf?" Dana shook her head.

"Well, George and Martha lived in Sarasota, Florida, and it was a real scorcher of a day. But they both loved golf and they hadn't played for quite awhile, so they were absolutely committed that they were going to play all 18 holes, no matter what.

"After about six and a half hours, the golf pro noticed they hadn't come back in yet, and he got a little concerned. Another hour went by and pretty soon Martha makes an appearance at the soda machine.

'Boy, Martha,' the pro says. 'I was starting to worry about you two. What kept you so long?'

And Martha answers, 'Well, you know, we would have been back a lot sooner, but George had a heart attack at the 11th hole. And after that, it was hit the ball, drag George, hit the ball, drag George...'"

Dana laughed. "I get your point. Commitment, right?"

"Right."

"The story is kind of silly, but the point is serious. Commitment is a sacrifice you're willing to make and a risk you're willing to take. The biggest risk of all for most of us is rejection. It's the fear of being ridiculed by other people, especially people we love. You got a nice dose of that from your brother today."

"Yeah, I'm sure glad you showed up to talk me off the ledge," Dana remembered.

"Believe me, I wouldn't have wasted my time if I hadn't already known that you were committed, that you were willing to take the risk. Helen Keller said that life is either a daring adventure or nothing at all, that the only risk in life that's too great is not risking."

"Well, thanks for taking a chance on me," Dana said, gratefully.

"I'm glad to be here for you, while you're getting started. Right now, you need to borrow some of my strength. As you learn and grow in your business, you'll develop your own power. Pretty soon, you'll be lending your strength to your new distributors. You won't need me to blow up your balloon for you."

"I can't wait to feel that sure of myself." Dana said. "It'll be a very new feeling for me, that's for sure. Tell me the truth, does this rejection business ever really get easier?"

"Remember when we talked about how the mind is a magician?" Dana nodded. She loved that idea.

"If you think you can, you're right. If you think you can't, you're right, too—and you won't," Dana recited.

"Exactly. And your mind is the place where you handle rejection. In your mind, you have to create a space to win." counseled the Bag Lady.

"You mean with all those motivational tapes and self help books and stuff like that?" asked Dana.

"That's all very helpful. But I'm talking here about creating a specific framework for understanding and handling rejection.

"You might think of it as a numbers game. For instance, what if someone handed you a bucket of oysters and said there were three precious pearls in there. And what if you were told you could keep all the pearls you found—you just had to do the work. You'd start shucking—right?"

"Of course!" Dana responded.

"And what if you got half way through that bucket, and you still hadn't found any pearls. Would you quit?" the Bag Lady challenged.

"No, of course not. That would mean I was just getting that much closer to finding the oysters with the pearls."

"Same thing with this business. It's a numbers game. The more rejections you go through, the closer you are to finding those fabulous pearls for your business. I'll give you a great example.

"There's a wonderful couple named Bill and Peggy. They're very well known in this industry, very successful, huge! Here's what it took to get their very profitable business started.

"Now, remember, they knew quite a few people, so what they did in a year might take someone else a little longer, but that doesn't really matter. Just listen to the numbers: Bill and Peggy presented their business opportunity to more than 1,300 people in the first year."

Dana's eyes widened. That seemed like an awful lot of presentations. The Bag Lady read her reaction and reassured her.

"Relax. That may sound like a lot, but I know someone who talks to at least 20 people every day. That would add up to over 7,000 presentations in a year! It can be done.

"Anyway, out of the 1,300 presentations Bill and Peggy made, only 300 people signed up. And out of that 300, there were only 87 who actually did anything other than buy their products at a discount. And of those 87, there were only about 35 people who made any sincere effort at all to build a business.

Now, you might think Bill and Peggy didn't have much to show for all their effort. But you know what...out of that first year's batch of people, they ultimately made over $1 million from the efforts of just 11 of those original 1,300 people!"

"Wow!" whispered Dana. "11 from 1,300, that's...1,289 people who didn't really work out!"

"Very good," the Bag Lady nodded. "The point I'm making is, you mustn't take it personally when somebody doesn't accept the gift you're offering. Don't make yourself the issue. I like to look at it this way: 'Some will. Some won't. So what!' Stop whining. Start winning. Because, **someone's waiting!** Who's *next!?!*"

They were both laughing as the Bag Lady pulled up in front of the building for their first appointment. They quickly located apartment 2-B, the home of Valerie and Glenn Swanson. Glenn was once a good friend of Dana's ex and was the best man at their wedding. That was back before he'd even met Valerie. They'd drifted apart over the years, especially after Dana's husband started partying and staying out late. The couple greeted Dana and the Bag Lady warmly.

The events that followed were very similar to the party in Dana's apartment that morning. At the end of the tape, both Valerie and Glenn agreed they'd both like to drop some of their winter weight and decided to try a program.

As they chatted afterwards, the Bag Lady asked, "What kind of work do the two of you do?"

"We work for a small computer company," Glenn answered for both of them. "Val's a systems analyst and I work in purchasing."

"That's a pretty fast-paced world these days. Do you enjoy it?"

"We used to," Val answered. "At least I did, anyway. But it's all gotten so competitive. Acquisitions, mergers, leapfrog technology. New companies starting up and others shutting down right and left. There's so much paranoia at work, it makes my head hurt."

"Yeah, frankly, we've been a little concerned about both of us working at the same place. It's not a very stable environment. And we're putting all our eggs in one basket. Makes me more than nervous," Glenn added.

"I can imagine," said the Bag Lady. "If the car industry behaved like the computer industry over the past few years, a Rolls-Royce would cost $5, get 300 miles to the gallon and blow up once a year!

Everyone laughed. "What about you?" Valerie asked. "Do you enjoy this kind of work?"

"Are you kidding! I've got the greatest boss in the world, Dahling..." the Bag Lady giggled. "Me."

"Seriously," she continued. "They say if you choose a job you love you'll never work a day in your life. That's really how I feel—I love my work. And," she added, "I *only* work with people I choose—people I really like!"

Dana beamed. "And I get to have the greatest mentor in the world!"

"Sounds ideal," Val observed. "I think the only thing my boss cares about is controlling costs and covering his butt with the big shots upstairs."

"In that case, maybe you can help us out," said the Bag Lady. "It sounds like you probably have a co-worker or two who might be seriously looking for a change. We are looking for good people. We need help handling the growth in our business. If you know someone who might be interested, I'd really appreciate your letting us know," said the Bag Lady, as always, planting seeds.

"You're looking to hire some new employees?" Glenn asked.

"Not employees. Business partners."

"Really? What kind of background are you looking for?" Glenn asked, sounding genuinely curious.

"Oh, I grow my own," she smiled. "Seriously, the training is free. You'd be amazed at the diverse backgrounds of the people in this business."

"But listen, we've got to run to our next appointment. We can talk again later if you like. For now, let's just get you started properly on your weight management program. We'll be talking to you tomorrow!"

Dana and the Bag Lady said their good-byes and were soon out the door. In the car, an excited Dana had many questions.

"Wow, that was so great! Two more customers! But you know, I had the feeling Val and Glenn might be interested in the business opportunity, too. Why didn't we talk more about that with them?"

"Excellent question, Dana! For one thing, this is a business and businesses run on time. Tonight, we happen to have a very tight schedule. That's a nice problem to have, by the way."

"I consider my time very valuable, and I'm sure those people who are still waiting to see us also value their time. And it's downright rude to keep them waiting.

"The other reason I didn't launch into a full scale discussion of the business right away, is something I call 'situation sensitivity.' You might want to write this down." Dana scrambled for her notebook.

"A new person learning this business has a tendency to spill all their candy in the lobby," the Bag Lady continued. "The minute we find a warm body who's kind enough to hold still for five minutes, we want to tell them every single thing we know about the business in our very first conversation."

"Did you ever notice how God gave us two ears and only one mouth?" Dana nodded.

"That's because we should listen twice as much as we talk," the Bag Lady counseled. "When we listen more, we learn more about what the other person wants and needs, so we have a better understanding of 'which itch to scratch.' That's situation sensitivity. See what I mean?"

"I think so." Dana said, all ears.

"Good. Now, what did we learn about Glenn and Valerie tonight that may give us a clue about which itch they might like scratched?" asked the Bag Lady.

"Well," Dana thought out loud, nibbling the eraser on her pencil. "They seemed a little nervous about job security. And Val didn't seem all that happy with her boss either."

"Very good. What else?"

"I was just thinking that Glenn seemed to perk up a little when you mentioned the thing about looking for partners. Maybe he'd like to be in his own business," Dana observed.

"Right again. And don't overlook the obvious. They both were interested in getting the kinds of results our products provide. You and I both know they're going to be impressed with the products, right?"

"Definitely!" stated Dana.

"And once that happens, they're going to be much more receptive to the business potential of those products. So, when you and I follow up with them to check on their product results, we're probably going to find them in an even more open frame of mind than they were tonight. Just stands to reason."

"I get what you mean," said Dana. "When they love our products, they're more likely to love the business opportunity, too!"

"I wouldn't want anyone in my business who didn't love the products. And until they do, we don't really have anything to talk about, do we? We'll call them tomorrow and let them know about our conference call."

"You know," mused Dana, "This kind of reminds me of when I was little and my grandpa would take me fishing. I was always in such a rush to catch something. I'd keep checking my line and changing my bait and asking him if we shouldn't move to a better spot. I was such a nuisance. He said the only bait I needed was patience if I wanted to catch fish."

"You're right. It's a lot like that. The situation sensitivity part of it is knowing which bait to use and choosing the right spot at the right time when the fish are feeding. Then you just have to throw your hook out there and wait for the fish to see something it wants now."

They parked for their next appointment. It went smoothly, as did the remaining two of the evening. By the time it was all said and done, they had a total of seven new people on products and four very solid prospects for the business opportunity.

When they got back to Dana's apartment, the Bag Lady pulled out the scorecard she had referred to earlier as "figs and gauges." Together, they totaled up their accomplishments for the day.

They had spoken to 15 new people, hosted a home party, gotten products into 12 people's bodies, showed the video five times, signed up a preferred customer (who probably would become a distributor), booked another home party and retailed over $800 in products!

"Not bad for your first day!" the Bag Lady congratulated her new partner.

"And my 48-hour plan is only half over!" Dana rejoiced. "Just imagine if tomorrow is this good!"

"And what if you did this well every day for a whole week?

"Even if you only worked six days out of seven, that would be over $5,000 in sales for one week. If you only earned 20 percent on all of it after splitting profits with party hosts and new distributors, that's still $1,000. When was the last time you made that much in one week?" asked the Bag Lady.

"Wow! Never! Hey, what if I could do that every week! That's over $50,000 a year!" Dana realized.

"You're right. And, that's just the beginning. You keep this up and you'll be ready for 'royalty' in no time at all."

"The true keys to your kingdom are in the royalty overrides," the Bag Lady explained. "We haven't even talked about that yet. But we will. For now, just think of it this way: If you had the opportunity to choose between opening up your own McDonald's franchise and making 10 cents on every burger, or having stock in the company and earning one hundredth of a cent on every hamburger sold by the whole company, which would you rather have?"

Dana was struggling with mental math as the Bag Lady let herself out the front door. Just before she heard the latch click, Dana heard the Bag Lady repeat playfully, "Royalty. Think royalties…"

Dana was so excited, she could hardly think about sleeping. If it weren't so late, she thought, she could be on the phone right now. She occupied herself instead with straightening her perpetually cluttered kitchen.

The day's mail was still neatly stacked on the counter near the phone where she'd left it earlier in the day. She flipped through it absentmindedly. An envelope caught her eye.

It was obviously from some insurance company, warning her about all the terrible things that might befall her and the children for which they were not covered. Despite the intended scare tactics, the teaser line on the outside of the envelope struck her with an entirely different interpretation tonight. It read…

"What if…"

CHAPTER SIX
Obstacles and Opportunities

The alarm clock sounded next to Dana's bed, but she couldn't hear it from the next room. She was still slumped in the rocking chair next to Kevin's crib, one arm draped over the rail, her hand resting on his broad little back. She'd fallen asleep patting him. He'd had a rough night.

This was the second episode in the past month. He'd awakened in the middle of the night coughing violently, making coarse barking sounds like a baby seal. The strange noises coming out of his little mouth frightened him almost as much as they did Dana. And the more scared he got, the more he coughed. The more he coughed, the more difficult it was for him to breathe. After one particularly hard spell of coughing, he was exhausted from lack of oxygen.

The baby had been prone to viral infection since infancy, and Dana knew the drill all too well. Her ears were trained to wake at the first symptomatic bark, and she would quickly rouse herself to run the shower, filling the bathroom with hot steam. Then, she would sit on the edge of the tub with the baby in her lap, letting him breath in the soothing vapors until gradually his coughing would subside.

When the crisis had passed, she would place him in his crib and set up the vaporizer next to it, with a high backed chair on the opposite side. She fashioned a makeshift tent by draping a blanket across the crib rails and over the chair back, trapping the moist air inside. All this helped to ease the inflammation in Kevin's lungs and usually allowed him to sleep peacefully. But Dana was afraid to leave him like that, and usually fell asleep in the chair beside him.

It was the ruckus in the hall when the neighbor kids left for school that woke her.

School! Oh no, Her daughter was going to be late again. Katie hated that. And what about her meeting with the Bag Lady? She'd never make it into the city by nine o'clock. And what about her 48 hour plan? She just couldn't blow it!

She roused Katie and told her to hurry. Katie shot her a scornful look when she learned she was late for school, but dutifully turned her attention to dressing herself. Meanwhile, Dana dialed the Plaza, feeling overwhelmed. Just as the Bag Lady answered, the doorbell rang.

"Hello, it's me, Dana, I'm so sorry—could you hold on just one second. Someone's at the door…"

She bounded through the living room, peered through the peep hole—the baby-sitter, of course.

"I'm so sorry," Dana said opening the door for the sitter and ushering her in. "I'm running really late. Kevin's sick again. Wait a minute, will you, I'm on the phone." She raced back across the apartment and picked up the phone, out of breath.

"I'm back. I'm so sorry." Dana pushed the words out between breaths. "I'm not going to be able make it this morning. I was up all night with the baby. I've got to get him to a doctor right away. Katie's late for school. I feel terrible about this…"

"Settle down, Dahling," the Bag Lady sounded firm but reassuring. "This is me you're talking to—remember? I'm a mom, too. Now listen, take care of your challenge. Get Katie off to school, find out when the doctor can see little Kevin, and then call me, okay?"

"Okay…Thanks." Dana felt better already. Thank goodness the Bag Lady understood that the kids were always her first priority. She'd never had a boss who seemed to get that one. She hung up and took a long deep breath.

"Cindy, I guess you heard what's going on. I'm not going to need you to sit this morning, but could you possibly take Katie to school. She's missed her bus and I can't take little Kevin out, sick as he is. I promise I'll make it up to you."

The baby-sitter sighed, looking a little put out.

"You know Dana, this is beginning to wear a little thin," she said, making sure Dana got her meaning. "Come on Katie, are you ready to go?"

"Wait…she hasn't eaten anything. I think I have a breakfast bar in here somewhere," Dana muttered as she rummaged through the cabinet. "Here, honey, eat this on your way, okay?"

"I don't like that kind, Mommy. I want Kangaroo Krunchies for breakfast," Katie whined.

"Katie, honey," Dana said, kneeling down cupping Katie's face in her hands. "I know you hate to be late. If you take time for a bowl of cereal you'll be even more late.

"Hey, here's an idea. I'll put some in a sandwich bag and you can eat them like a snack while you're walking to school. How's that?" Dana negotiated.

Katie nodded her head with a resigned sigh. What a rotten breakfast, Dana thought. What a rotten mother, she added to her already guilt-laden thoughts.

As the door slammed shut, Dana was dialing the clinic. The voice that answered sounded hassled.

"Middleville Health Center, may I help you?"

Dana pleaded her case and begged for an early appointment, but the spring flu season had already packed the waiting room to capacity.

"I'm sorry, you'll just have to come in and wait. The doctors are still at the hospital on rounds, there's only one here, so it could be quite awhile," the receptionist said, sounding like she'd repeated that phrase too many times already that morning.

Dana had to do better than that. "Look, I understand what you're saying, but it's really important I get my baby in to see the doctor soon. He's very ill, and I hate to expose him to all those other sick people in the waiting room."

"I'm very sorry. There's nothing...hold please."

Dana was suddenly in that phone limbo called "on hold." She resigned herself to waiting and started preparing a bottle of juice for Kevin with the phone receiver held tight between her ear and shoulder. The doorbell rang again. She gave up on clinic, hung up the phone and headed for the door.

The landlord stood waiting in the hall. He didn't look very happy. Oh great, thought Dana ruefully, I really need this today.

"Mr. Feeney, I know I'm a little behind with the rent right now, but I promise to get it caught up soon. Honest. I haven't been able to find work and the child support check hasn't come for two months and..."

Dana knew she was babbling, but couldn't seem to stop herself, even though her story was obviously making no impression on Mr. Feeney. Just then, little Kevin woke up crying. His voice was tight and hoarse.

"There's the baby, would you excuse me just one second?"

She motioned for Mr. Feeney to step inside as she raced to the baby's rescue. By now he was coughing again, and his crying took on a scared tone. She picked him up. He was hot with fever and his diaper was soaked. Poor little guy. Mr. Feeney had wandered into the baby's room behind her. His expression had softened a little.

"Is he all right?" he asked. "That cough sounds pretty rough."

"It's the croup again. Third time this year. I was just calling the doctor for an appointment when you rang the bell." She was swaying her body and patting the baby's back soothingly. Feeney could see she was near tears. Not much sleep either, he surmised. The scene pulled at his heart.

Dana marshaled her last shred of energy and faced her landlord, holding the baby close for courage.

"Mr. Feeney, I know you must be tired of my excuses by now. But I really believe I'll be able to straighten things out with you soon. I just got started with a new business. I'm turning my life around. Honest."

The landlord rubbed his scruffy chin, thinking. He really hated having to play tough guy with his tenants—especially the ones who were struggling like Dana.

"Honest, Mr. Feeney. I made almost $100 yesterday in my new business! I'm probably going to need most of that today for the doctor, but I promise I'll have something for you by next week," Dana pleaded.

He thought he must be going crazy. He'd been renting apartments for 13 years now, and he'd heard it all many times before. Still, something made him want to believe Dana. Well, what difference would another week make?

"Look," he said. "I'm not a bad guy. I got kids too, ya' know. They gotta eat, too. I'll give you a break, Dana. You got till the first of the month. Next Thursday. That's the best I can do."

Dana thanked him through tears of relief. Maybe things were starting to go her way after all. She changed the baby's diaper and held him on one hip while she dialed the Bag Lady once again.

"That's great!" the Bag Lady responded when she heard about the wait in the doctor's office. "I'll pick you up and we'll drive to the clinic. You don't want to haul that sick baby around on a bus. We'll have lots of time to talk while you're waiting to see the doctor."

Dana hung up, dazed in amazement. Her new mentor seemed to see everything in such a positive way. Things she saw as obstacles, the Bag Lady made into opportunities. Dana pondered—there must be some connection between the woman's dauntless attitude and her extraordinary success.

By the time the Bag Lady arrived, Dana had the baby all bundled up, the diaper bag loaded, and her spirits stoked-up as well. She was actually smiling as she climbed into the impressive looking Infinity coupe her new friend had rented. By the time they pulled into the clinic's parking lot, Dana had fully briefed her on the morning's events.

There was only a single vacant chair in the crowded waiting room. The Bag Lady held little Kevin in her lap while Dana signed in at the reception desk. The nurse informed her of what she already knew; only one of the doctors had come in so far. It was going to be a long wait.

Dana came back stifling a yawn, and the Bag Lady rose from the chair, motioning for Dana to take it and the baby.

"Here, I think you need this more than I do this morning." Dana accepted without protest. Her sleepless night was definitely catching up with her.

"I think you could use a lift. Here, let me make a pick-you-up," the Bag Lady offered and scurried off to find a water cooler without waiting for an answer.

As she walked, she was searching her bag for what turned out to be small sample packets of the energy capsules. She soon returned, handing the glass and the capsules to Dana, who accepted them eagerly.

"This is just what I need!"

A little boy standing next to his mother nearby was watching her.

"Me have some...?" he wanted to know? Before his mother could jump in, the Bag Lady quickly responded.

"These vitamins only for mommies, especially mommies who didn't get enough sleep."

His mother soon distracted him with a small bag of animal crackers she'd brought along. But she herself was clearly intrigued with "the mommy capsules" the Bag Lady had mentioned.

"So, somebody's invented sleep in a pill?" she wanted to know.

"You could look at it that way. Tell her about the first time you tried it, Dana." The Bag Lady said, passing the ball to her protégé.

Without thinking about what she was saying, Dana simply related her first experience with the product. She told about her original skepticism and her amazement at the results.

The other woman seemed intrigued. "Boy, that sounds like something I could definitely use. Where can you get it?"

"Oh, you know what, I'm sure I have a few extra samples with me. I wouldn't dream of traveling without it. Would you like to try it?" the Bag Lady offered.

The woman readily accepted. By this time, it was apparent that several other women in the waiting room had been observing the whole scene with curiosity. The Bag Lady shot Dana a "watch this" look and caught the eye of one of these women, who also had a child in tow.

"Would you like to try it, too? Don't worry, it's just vitamins. Anyone else? This whole room looks like it could use a little lift."

Two more women accepted her offer and one declined. It was obvious the third woman didn't trust anything— especially something like "sleep-in-a-pill." That clearly sounded too good to be true. But she watched the others with guarded interest.

As she served the other women, the Bag Lady briefly answered their questions and told her story about how she kicked her two-pot-per-day coffee habit. Then she sat back down to resume her conversation with Dana.

"You know, Dana, one of the things I've always really appreciated about my business, is that it allows me the flexibility to be a good mom and still earn as much as a Fortune 500 CEO, and all from my kitchen table. When you have children, your life is never very predictable. You're always going to suddenly need to care for a sick child, attend a parent-teacher conference, bake cookies for the cub scouts…Whatever. Whenever.

"I think of my life as a jar of marbles." The Bag Lady reached in her big black bag and dug out a mason jar filled to the top with brightly colored marbles. She immediately attracted the interest of the little boy next to her. He quickly rose from where he was playing on the floor and came over.

"Sweetie, would you like to help me?" she asked. He nodded wordlessly, wide eyes on the marbles. The Bag Lady handed him an empty plastic cup.

"Would you go fill this cup at the water cooler over there and bring it back to me?" The child eagerly rose to the challenge and soon returned with the water. His mother, of course, was paying very close attention.

"Most of us have lives that are already very full, like this jar. Think of each of these marbles as the dozens of cares and responsibilities that we cram into every day. It looks like there isn't enough room in this jar for a single thing more, am I right?"

The little boy's mother couldn't resist jumping in: "Boy, that describes my life to a Tee!"

The Bag Lady smiled at her, pleased to include her in the conversation. "And that's on a good day—right?

"I was just explaining to Dana how our business works so well for busy people, especially moms like us." Now the Bag Lady took the glass of water and poured it into the jar.

"But you see, you can fit this water into the jar, can't you? This business is like the water. You fit it into the empty spaces between the marbles."

One of the other women in the waiting room chimed in. "You're obviously not talking about my business. If my husband and I aren't there at the car wash taking care of our customers every single day, we lose money." Then she added, "And if today's visit confirms my suspicions, I don't know how we'll manage. My last pregnancy kept me in bed for four months." Her remarks explained the pale and weary look on her face.

"You poor dear. That's pretty scary, isn't it?" The Bag Lady's sympathy was sincere.

"You know," the Bag Lady continued, "I was eight months into a high risk pregnancy myself, with another child five years old, when I decided to try this business. I had less than no income, hopelessly in debt, and I was sitting in a welfare office, because my doctor turned me away for unpaid bills. How was I supposed to support my family in that condition?

"But you know what? By the time my baby arrived just one month later, I'd put thousands of dollars in my pocket."

Now everyone in the waiting room was listening.

"What exactly do you do?" the little boy's mother wanted to know. The child was maneuvering himself into the Bag Lady's lap now, still fascinated by the marbles in the jar she was holding.

"Is it all right if I give him a few of these marbles to play with?" The Bag Lady asked.

"Well, I guess if he promises not to put them in his mouth. Okay, Tommy?"

The child nodded wholeheartedly. The Bag Lady dug a few marbles out of the jar and placed them in a small blue felt bag with a drawstring which she had materialized from somewhere in the recesses of her big bag. She handed it to Tommy.

"Keep them in this little bag, Tommy, so they won't roll away and get lost." She smiled warmly. Looking up at the child's mother, she added, "Now you know why my friends call me the Bag Lady."

"Have you ever heard of network marketing?" she asked Tommy's mother. The woman thought for a moment.

The pregnant woman chimed in again: "Is that like Amway?"

"That's not the company I'm with, but Amway is the granddaddy of all network marketing companies. Do you know it's almost 30 years old and still doubled its sales in the past two years? I think they're at somewhere around $7 billion a year now, worldwide."

"Wow, you're kidding!" Another women came to life now, piping up for the first time since she'd tried her energy capsules. "A friend of mine said she got hurt by another company. She ended up with a garage full of stuff she couldn't sell."

"I hear you," the Bag Lady answered. "Some people don't make it work, for whatever reason. But then again, have you ever known anyone else who tried starting a business and it didn't work out?"

"Sure," the car wash lady volunteered. "Most new businesses fail in the first couple of years. I read that in *Success Magazine*. I can tell you, it was pretty touch and go for us in the car wash business more than a few times. Still is!"

"You're exactly right," said the Bag Lady. "And even if your business had gone under, it wouldn't have meant you were wrong to go for it. I think we often develop success from our failures; we learn from them and we grow from them. It was Mary Pickford who said failure is not in the falling down, but the staying down.

"Speaking for myself, I've made some poor choices in my own career; I've picked some business opportunities that weren't right for me. But think about it—if you waste your money on one horrible movie, do you quit going to movies? If you suffered through one miserable date, would you swear off men?"

"I can relate to that!" Dana chimed in. "How about one disastrous marriage!"

"So, you get what I mean." She shot Dana a knowing grin. "I'm just very grateful that, in spite of a few unfortunate experiences, I didn't quit. I was still crystal clear that network marketing is the future. Is my future. Probably by the year 2005, even Oprah will be doing it. I mean, who would have dreamed that eight years ago I was glad just to be able to buy day-old bread and marked-down produce, and today, I'm financially free."

"I'm sorry, I have trouble relating to numbers like that," said the woman with the friend in Amway.

"I know exactly what you mean," the Bag Lady agreed. "You know, I used to teach school in Brooklyn, and in a whole month I never made much more than $1,000. But what I've learned over the years is that you have to keep rewriting your goals."

The women in the waiting room had been listening attentively. Only two people had been called into the examination rooms since Dana and the Bag Lady arrived. Now, the nurse was calling little Tommy and his mother. As they left the room, the car wash woman turned her full attention to finding out more about this "business" she'd been hearing about.

"I'd really like to know more about this. What's involved? Do you have to sell anything?" she wanted to know.

"Dana, tell her about yesterday," the Bag Lady prompted.

Proudly, Dana related her experience: how she told her friends about what she was doing, just two days before, about the party at her house the previous morning, and how much she accomplished in just two days.

"I've already made over $100 and I just got started day before yesterday!" Her voice rang with excitement.

"And when you were doing all this, did it feel like you were selling anything?" the Bag Lady asked.

"Oh no! They were asking me about it. Just like you and the other people here at the clinic have been doing since we arrived."

"You see how it is, Dahling? If my success depended on finding people who wanted to sell, my business wouldn't be half the size it is. Very few people like to sell.

"This business isn't about closing people—it's about opening people. It's about changing lives by opening people's minds to new possibilities."

"You sound like you really enjoy your work," observed the car wash lady. "I haven't felt that way about mine for a long time."

"I wouldn't be doing it if I didn't love it!

"Did you ever read a book by Kahlil Gibran, called *The Prophet?*" The woman was shaking her head. It's one of my favorites," the Bag Lady said. "There's a great line in it about work. It says that 'work is love made visible. If you cannot work with love, but only distaste, it's better to be a beggar at the gate of the temple and take donations from those who work with joy'. That's the way I feel."

"Speaking of feeling...," offered the woman from the car wash. "I have to admit I'm feeling a lot better than when I came in. What did you call that stuff you gave us to try?"

Just then, the nurse was calling her name to go into the examining room.

The Bag Lady reached into her bag and pulled out a videotape. "Here, why don't you take a look at this. It explains a little about our products and I think you'll also see where the opportunity to make money comes from. See what you think. Afterwards, if you want to know more, give us a call here in New York—Dana's number is right there. If not, just do me a favor and mail it back to me. My address and phone number are on the tape."

The woman thanked the Bag Lady sincerely. She actually seemed to be smiling as she walked out of the room. It was a noticeable contrast to the mood she had displayed when she arrived.

"Do you think I could borrow that tape next?" asked the other woman, who'd been fairly quiet until now.

"You know, I have another one back at my office. Why don't you write down your name, address and phone number for me, and I'll get it mailed out to you right away." The Bag Lady gave the woman an index card and a pen from her bag. As she was writing down the information, the Bag Lady asked her what interested her most about what they'd been discussing.

"I just need to make some changes, that's all. I really don't feel like talking about it right now, okay?" she responded. It was obvious she was troubled about something.

"Of course, I understand. I think you'll be able to relate to some of the stories on that tape." The Bag Lady smiled.

When it was time for Dana to bring little Kevin in to see the doctor, the Bag Lady remained in the waiting room. After a little while, Tommy and his mother came back out. Both of them were wearing big smiles.

"Thanks so much for these vitamins!" the woman chirped. "What did you say it was?"

"Did you like it?"

"It did the trick. How can I get more?" the woman inquired.

"Glad you asked! Here, let me give you a catalog." As the Bag Lady retrieved the catalog from her bag, she added, "You know, ordinarily I keep a few things in the trunk of my car—it seems I'm always running into someone who wants some right away. But I happen to be traveling right now, so I'm driving a rented car. But you can order it for yourself with no problem. Here, what you had is right on page 13." The Bag Lady explained to the woman how to order directly over the company's 800 number using a credit card and a PIN.

"You should receive this in a few days. By the way, do you know anyone who's interested in losing weight? We've got a fantastic weight management product!"

"Well, I'd love to lose about 20 pounds myself. But I just don't believe any of those things really work....Do they?"

"Well, I don't know about 'any of those things,' but I do know what our product did for me. In fact, I can show you. Here, look." The Bag Lady had already pulled her "before picture" from the bag and showed it to the woman.

"That's you?" she asked, astonished.

"That's me—about 60 pounds ago. I'm still what you might call 'under construction.' But I can tell you this much: Back before this picture was taken, I told my husband it was lights out forever. I'd been fighting and losing the diet wars for decades, and I'd just about decided I was never going to know what it was like for my arms to stop moving when I did."

The other woman laughed.

"The first day I tried this product, I knew this time it was going to be different. I'd be glad to give you a sample to try if you're serious about losing the weight."

"Oh, I'm definitely serious!"

"Great! All I ask is that you give me your phone number, so either my partner, Dana, or I can check in with you and make sure it's working properly. Deal?"

The Bag Lady offered to walk Tommy and his mother to their car and on the way explained how to use the sample and took the necessary information from the woman, whose name she learned was Cleo.

Just as the Bag Lady was saying good-bye to little Tommy, Dana came out of the building with Kevin and waved to them both.

"How's the baby? What did the doctor say?" the Bag Lady called out from across the parking lot.

"He's going to be just fine," Dana answered and smiled down at her sleepy but contented baby sucking on his chubby thumb.

"And wait 'til I tell you!" she said excitedly, approaching the car. "This is so great. I got on the doctor's scale while I was waiting in the examining room and I couldn't believe my eyes. I've lost three pounds since the day before yesterday when you gave me that sample!" Dana bubbled.

"Wait, were you using a sample like this?" Cleo asked, holding up the packet the Bag Lady had just given her.

"That's the one," Dana answered.

Cleo turned to the Bag Lady. "Since I'm calling in an order anyway, what if I ordered this weight loss stuff, too. I can do that, right?"

"Sure, you might as well. It's satisfaction guaranteed, so you really have nothing to lose," she answered. "Except..."

"Except fat!" all three of them spoke at once—laughing.

On the way back to Dana's house, little Kevin slept, making it easy for the women to talk.

"You saw how we did that?" the Bag Lady asked Dana with a triumphant grin.

"That was awesome! I can't believe how fast this is going. I feel like my whole life is changing before my eyes," Dana beamed. "And after this day started out looking so horrible, too!"

"It's all in the way you look at things, isn't it," the Bag Lady observed. "Your perception is your reality, Dahling. You just proved that today."

"Tell you what, I'm getting hungry. How about you? Could you handle a little Chinese?" the Bag Lady asked as she pulled into the packed parking lot of a small Chinese restaurant.

Although the restaurant was crowded, they were seated without much of a wait. As they studied their menus, a harried looking waiter appeared at their table.

"Would you like me to tell you the specials, ladies?"

The waiter pointed out a couple of favorite selections and they both chose the sizzling vegetables, along with steaming bowls of hot and sour soup. As they waited for their food, they chatted about the morning's events.

"Do you see what I meant about "water around marbles, Dana? You made a sale and picked up two really promising new prospects without doing much of anything out of the ordinary. You didn't compromise your values or take time away from anything that's important to you. You just went about the normal course of your life, showing interest and concern for others and speaking your truth.

"So, who doesn't have time to do that?" the Bag Lady concluded.

Dana happily agreed.

The food arrived and they both attacked their meals with enthusiasm. Baby Kevin was more than delighted with his bowl of lo-mein noodles, and he was soon stuffing messy fistfuls into his mouth with abandon. As seems typical with toddlers, he'd enjoyed a miraculous and nearly instantaneous recovery the moment he entered the examining room.

His fever was gone now, his appetite had obviously returned, and the only sign of his illness was a slightly runny nose.

"I can see how relieved you are that Kevin's feeling better. Did Katie get croup, too, when she was a baby?" the Bag Lady asked.

"No, thank God." Dana said with obvious relief. "He apparently inherits the tendency from me, at least according to my mother. Katie's more prone to allergy attacks—and, of course, the secondary infections that develop when her allergies are acting up a lot. I'm sure the ventilation in that rattletrap old building of ours is only aggravating her problems. But right now, I can barely even afford to live there, much less someplace better." Dana studied her empty bowl.

"Where would you like to live?" the Bag Lady asked quietly.

Dana looked up wistfully as the picture formed in her head. "Oh, you know, the usual. A place of our own in a nice neighborhood with other children. A yard. Their very own bedrooms. Good school nearby. A quiet street with not much traffic...The same things everybody probably wants for their kids."

"I'd also add that I want my kids to live in a free country," the Bag Lady said. "In a society without hatred, in a world at peace—but I'll bet you and I are on the same wavelength with that, too, am I right?"

Dana smiled and nodded. Before long, the waiter came to collect their plates, and the Bag Lady asked for the check.

Later, as she was filling in the tip on the credit card charge slip, she casually asked the waiter, "Say I was thinking. In your line of work, you probably come across a lot of customers who are concerned with eating in a more healthy way, watching their calories, their fat and cholesterol—right?"

The waiter agreed it was a topic of great interest.

"Perhaps you can help me then," the Bag Lady continued. "My business involves helping people live healthier lives. I've personally helped hundreds of people lose weight, increase their energy and improve their overall health."

"I'm looking for help with my business, and I also pay commissions for referrals. If you're interested in some extra income, or possibly even a position in my business, please give me a call."

She handed the waiter her business card and got up to leave. Dana busied herself with gathering up the baby's things. The waiter, obviously intrigued, studied the card for a moment. Suddenly, a female voice rang out from the adjacent booth.

"Excuse me. A minute, before you go, I've got to ask you…" the woman said, approaching the Bag Lady.

"I couldn't help overhearing you mention weight loss. What have you got? I'm really desperate. I've tried everything but wiring my jaw shut and the doctor says I'm a walking time bomb 'til I get some of this flab off my hips and heart."

The Bag Lady smiled with genuine understanding. "I know exactly what you mean," she said, reaching into her bag. Once again, she retrieved her "before" picture and showed it to the woman.

"This is me, 60 pounds ago. Up to that time, I'm sure I tried everything you've tried—and then some, probably. Now, I have something that really works. I'll guarantee it 100%. We've got to run right now, but why don't you give me a call later."

The Bag Lady jotted down the telephone number of the Plaza on her business card along with Dana's name and number. She didn't want to make this woman wait—her life might be hanging in the balance.

"I'm staying at this number in the city until Sunday. Or, you can always call my partner, Dana. Here's her number. If you're really serious about this, give us a call." She smiled directly into the woman's eyes and then turned to leave. "Oh, by the way, let me start you off with a free sample, so you can start using the product right away. Do you have a business card?

Just as they were leaving the restaurant, Dana suddenly stopped.

"Wait! We forgot our fortune cookies!" She started back to the table to retrieve the cellophane-wrapped cookies, only to find the waiter there offering the cookies to her from a small plastic tray. He bowed. Dana bowed back, taking the cookies and smiling at the waiter.

Dana had a substantial collection of the tiny white slips of paper she'd saved from every fortune cookie she'd ever eaten stuffed in her wallet. Today's was bound to be special, she thought.

She offered the Bag Lady her choice of the two cookies, and proceeded to unwrap hers as they walked out to the parking lot. With practiced hands, she snapped the cookie in two and retrieved the crumpled paper, unfolding it gingerly. As she read the fortune, she was smiling and nodding in agreement. It said:

> "In order to get where you want to go,
> you first have to leave where you are."

CHAPTER SEVEN
The Art of Duplication

Dana was still repeating the fortune in her head as they buckled the baby and then themselves into their seat belts. Turning the key in the ignition, the Bag Lady announced, "We're on our way, Dahling!"

By the time they arrived at Dana's apartment, Kevin was slumped in one of those impossible positions only accomplished by sleeping babies in car seats. As soon as she had safely deposited him in his crib, Dana rejoined the Bag Lady in the kitchen.

"What's that dejected look on your face, Dana? I thought we were having a pretty terrific day!"

"Oh, you're right. It's certainly much better than I expected when I got up this morning. But here we are, stuck at my house for the afternoon while my 48 hour plan is supposed to be in full gear. Katie will be home in an hour, and I gave my sitter the day off when the baby got sick."

"You're doing it again, Dana."

"What? I'm doing what again?" Dana asked, her face all scrunched up.

"It's called 'making-a-living-thinking.' You're putting limits on what's possible. You're letting circumstances dictate what you can and can't accomplish. Big mistake. Huge!" The Bag Lady was digging in her bag again.

"Here." She handed Dana an object that resembled a small telescope. Dana turned it over and around in her hands, fascinated.

"It's a kaleidoscope. Here, look inside." Dana held the smaller end to her eye and a delighted "Ohhh" escaped from her mouth.

"Oh, I remember these! I turn it, right? How does this one work?"

She drew the kaleidoscope away from her face long enough to examine it. "Oh, I see. You turn it this way. Wow, look at that! Oh, Katie would love this!" She was lost for the moment in the shifting, cascading, ever-changing colors.

"Let me know when you see the pattern repeat itself," the Bag Lady instructed.

"Oh, but that's the thing with kaleidoscopes! They're always changing. Different. They never repeat!" objected Dana.

"But there must be some limit to how many different patterns it can create," the Bag Lady argued back.

"No, I don't think so," said Dana very seriously. "I think the possibilities are limitless. Like snowflakes."

"Really! Imagine that, Dahling! Limitless possibilities!" the Bag Lady quipped.

Dana took the kaleidoscope away from her eye and looked at the Bag Lady with a sheepish grin.

"Thank you. I got it. You want me to imagine there are no limits to what's possible?"

"Wrong," said the Bag Lady emphatically. "I don't want you to imagine anything. I want you to believe. To *know* it with your whole being.

"If the random behavior of simple bits of broken colored glass in this little contraption can be limitless—then you've got to *know* that a magnificent, infinitely complex, God-made creature like yourself, must be 1,000 times, 10,000 times, a million times more limitless!"

"Did I hear somebody attempting to explain infinity?" asked a voice from the living room. Almost immediately, a face followed the voice into the kitchen. It was Linda with her 3-year old in tow.

"I stopped by to see how the baby's doing. What did the doctor say?"

"The usual. Rest, lots of liquids, no dairy products for awhile, blah blah blah. What did your husband say about the business?"

"Don't worry about him. He's going to love the idea. In fact, he'll probably think it was his own idea after my party tonight."

"Wait a minute!" said a startled Dana. "Did you say tonight!"

"No time like the present, right? It's no big deal—just a bunch of women from the building and some of the other mothers from Mikey's daycare center. Oh, and my two sisters and my cousin. Is that too many at one time?" Linda asked with a self-satisfied smile.

"That should always be your worst problem, Dahling," the Bag Lady assured her in an equally self-satisfied fashion. "And to think Dear Dana here was concerned we weren't going to accomplish anything more today."

"But wait," Dana exclaimed. "I don't have anyone to look after Kevin and Katie tonight. It's my sitter's school night and I can't bring them along, with Kevin being sick."

"No problem." Linda quipped. "Already thought of it. If it's okay for me to bring Mikey over here tonight, my sitter said she'd watch all three of them for us. Deal?"

"Deal!" they cheered in unison.

"Linda, since you're here, maybe you'd like to stick around and learn a piece of the business I was going to show Dana this afternoon. This is *big*. This is where the gold is hidden. And for a lot of people, it's gold that never gets uncovered, just because they don't dig properly."

"Sounds important," Linda agreed. "I guess I could make some time. Will an hour be enough?"

"Perfect." The Bag Lady announced. And with that she went digging in her big black bag again. She emerged with a recipe box, the kind that holds index cards arranged alphabetically, and placed it dramatically on the table with a satisfied look.

"Now imagine this business is a cake. You want to create the finest cake ever made so what do you do? You buy the finest ingredients—right? The freshest eggs, the purest shortening, the finest flour. You mix it all together with the greatest of care and place it ever so carefully in the oven.

And you make everybody in the house walk softly, so the cake won't fall while it's baking.

"When the time's up, you open the oven and you take out your cake and guess what? It's flat. It's flat like a pancake! Tell me...what could be wrong?"

The two women thought for a moment. Linda volunteered, "Maybe you left something out, one of the ingredients perhaps?"

"Bingo! One of the ingredients is missing. Whatever makes the cake rise to its full size has been left out!" The Bag Lady was clearly enjoying this.

"Now, the ingredient that makes your business rise and grow is exactly what we're going to talk about, and it's called follow-up. Follow-up is where the fortune is. You'll see what I mean. Dana, where are all those scraps of paper you stuffed in your notebook with the names and addresses of people we talked to yesterday and today?"

Dana quickly produced her notebook.

The Bag Lady opened a recipe box. Inside, the index cards were all blank, and the pale blue divider tabs were numbered from 1-31 representing each day of the month. She took one of the index cards and showed Dana and Linda how to write in the basic information for the first name they found: Name, address, phone numbers for home and work.

The first name happened to be Susan's, from the party. They noted the date of the party and which products she had purchased. They also briefly described the results Susan was seeking from the products.

Dana and Linda watched as the Bag Lady dialed Susan's number. When she answered, the first question the Bag Lady asked her was whether she had a moment to talk.

Susan, apparently, was really glad to hear from her and happy to describe how she'd used her products that day and how she felt. The Bag Lady reinforced her experience warmly and reminded her what she should do next. She told Susan she'd call again in a couple of days to see how she was doing and said good-bye.

All told, the conversation lasted about 180 seconds.

"There, you see how I did that?" the Bag Lady beamed. "She was an easy one. Everything's going great and she had no questions. Now she feels reinforced—cared about and supported, because we were interested enough to make sure she was happy with what she bought—and she also knows that we'll keep our word about coaching her 'til she gets the results she's after on the products. She filed the card under the date a couple days off for the next follow-up call.

"Let's try another, shall we." She chose Glenn, one of the people to whom they'd shown the video the previous evening.

"Hello, may I speak to Glenn please?" There was silence as the Bag Lady waited for Glenn to come on the line. In the meantime, Dana darted into another room and brought back a cordless extension, so she could listen to both sides of the conversation. The Bag Lady noticed and smiled her approval with a broad "thumbs-up" gesture.

"Hi, Glenn, it's the Bag Lady from last night, remember?" Glenn returned her greeting.

"Dana and I are just following up with you this afternoon to make sure you've gotten started on your products properly.

"Hi, Glenn!" Dana chimed in.

"Have you got a moment to chat?" the Bag Lady asked.

"As long as it doesn't take much time. This place is a zoo today. We're in the middle of inventory," Glenn answered, sounding more than a little frazzled.

"In that case, it sounds like you'll really be needing all the extra energy you can get. I'm glad we got you started on our products when we did," the Bag Lady noted.

"We promise to be brief. Just tell us how you used your products today," the Bag Lady inquired.

"Just like you told me to," Glenn answered, somewhat evasively—he was obviously expecting some kind of sales-like pressure. "And to tell you the truth, I really haven't noticed any difference yet."

"Would you mind describing exactly what you used and when, Glenn. This is really important," the Bag Lady gently insisted.

"Okay. I took the powdered stuff before breakfast, and I took one of those little brown tablets with it."

"Ah! No wonder you haven't noticed any difference. I'm glad we got to talk, Glenn. It's very common for people to get things mixed up when they first start. No harm, though. Let me just quickly go over it with you one more time, okay?"

"Sure, but wait a second, let me write it down this time." Glenn made scrambling noises as he searched for a pencil. "Okay, go ahead."

The Bag Lady repeated the instructions, slowly and simply. "And Glenn, don't be surprised if you don't notice any results, even for the first few days. It took me a week to notice anything, but then within two weeks, I'd kicked a two pot-per-day coffee habit. Please, hang in there, I guarantee this will work for you. Okay?"

"Sure, no problem."

"We'll check in with you in a couple of days, Glenn. Bye now!"

The Bag Lady turned to Dana and Linda. "See, piece of cake. But just imagine what might have happened if we hadn't made that call. After a couple of days of using the products incorrectly, Glenn might have gotten discouraged and decided they didn't really work. Even if he never bothered to ask for a refund, it would be a terrible shame to deprive Glenn of his chance to experience the results he wanted—not to mention a wasted opportunity to create one more happy customer with another great story to tell."

The Bag Lady helped Dana as she filled out the index card for Glenn and noted the basics of their conversation. "Now let's file that away for another call tomorrow. We want to make sure he gets started right," she instructed.

"Now, since you have an extension phone here, we're going to train you on how to do the next one as a three-way call. That means we'll talk to your customer together. Later today, you'll call the phone company and order the three-way calling feature for your line. That way, we can make calls together any time, even when you and I are in different places."

She noticed that familiar "poverty look" cross Dana's face. "Relax, it's only four bucks a month at most. By the time it shows up on your bill, Dahling, it will have earned you much, much more than that! Three-way calling is a mainstay of our business. You need it. Not negotiable."

"Let's call Lonnie!" suggested Dana. "She was pretty psyched last night when we showed her the tape!"

"Great idea! Now, pay attention, Linda. You're going to help me with the next one. Here's how it goes:

"Dana, you make the call and get Lonnie on the line. Start out just the way we did with the others. Make sure she has a moment to talk. Explain why you're calling and let her know that I'm also on the line to help you, since you're new and just learning the business. Ask her to describe how she used her products today; and then you and I will handle the rest together, okay?"

Dana was already dialing the number. Lonnie was glad to hear from them and told them she was feeling very energized since taking her products that morning. But then she started asking for more details on what she was using as well as some of the other products in the catalog. She also wanted to know about ingredients and how the products she was using compared to others she had heard about. That's when the Bag Lady jumped in.

"You know, Lonnie, we really want to help you get your questions answered, and neither of us is a technical expert on these products. I only know about the great results people are getting." And the Bag Lady told her about a couple of people she personally knew.

"But we do have some brilliant people back at the home office who know this stuff inside and out. They've put together a toll-free product information hot line, fax-on-demand, and a website to answer questions like yours. Let me give you the numbers and website info. Got a pen?"

Lonnie gladly took down the information.

"After you call that 800 number, Lonnie, give us a call if you still have questions and we'll make sure you get them answered. Okay?" Lonnie agreed and they said a pleasant good-bye.

"What's this about an information hot line?" Dana wanted to know after they'd hung up. "You didn't mention that before!"

"Actually, I did touch on it. Remember yesterday when we were talking about choosing a company that's a four-legged horse, and I said the fourth leg on the horse was a strong support system?" Dana began flipping through her notes.

"Right! Here it is!" she said.

"That 800 number we just told Lonnie about is only a small part of our company's distributor support system.

"Write the name of this book down while you have your notes open. I want you to read it. It's called *Wave 3: the New Era in Network Marketing*. It's by a man I know, Richard Poe. It talks about how the leading-edge MLM company of today—what Richard calls the Wave 3 company—uses technology in many different ways to help distributors work more productively and become more successful, faster.

"For instance, did you notice how easy it was to handle Lonnie's question by giving her that 800 number. In the old days, we might have spent half an hour on the phone trying to explain things we aren't really all that knowledgeable about. Or worse still, we might have felt compelled to spend hours, or weeks or even months making ourselves into product experts on every conceivable question that might come up. That can slow your business down tremendously.

"And imagine how hard it would be for you to attract people to this business if they knew they had to study and learn about every one of the products and how they were developed and what this and that and this ingredient did and where they grew and...," the Bag Lady sat back in her chair to catch her breath.

"By giving Lonnie that 800 number, we empowered her to get the answer herself, directly from the experts themselves. Meanwhile, we can be making other calls or doing something else to grow our businesses. But, before we do another thing, I think you'd both better hear the message on the 800 number yourselves, don't you?"

They agreed and Dana quickly dialed the number. The Bag Lady handed the other receiver to Linda.

Both women broke into smiles as they listened to the message. It was upbeat and positive and contained lots of powerful testimonials mixed in with the hard information. The production quality was very professional and it lasted less than ten minutes.

"Wow! That was great!" Linda exclaimed.

"Yeah, I'll bet Lonnie will be impressed, even if it doesn't answer every single question she has."

"That's exactly right," the Bag Lady agreed. "When people ask a lot of questions, it doesn't necessarily mean they really want the answers. Sometimes they're just looking for reassurance that they've made a good decision. What they really want to hear is that the company is reputable, that the products have substance behind them and, that they really work. Wouldn't you say that recorded message does the job better than anything you might have said?"

"No question!" Dana agreed.

"And like I said, the Bag Lady added. "For a new person who's just getting started, like you two, it might take some time before you felt knowledgeable enough to handle questions on your own. That could really hold you back at first, slow you down. But tools like these—800 numbers, three-way calls with your sponsor, videotapes—like the one we've been using, and lots of other things we haven't even talked about yet—can help you get a much faster start."

"You mean there's more to the support system?" Linda wanted to know.

"You bet there is! For instance, I'm sure you know some people who are the 'seeing is believing' type. You know, skeptical about everything?"

"Like my brother," commented Dana.

"And lots of others. Now, don't you think they'd be just a little bit impressed if they could meet the owner of the company, visit corporate headquarters, hear what's going on from distributors all over the country, get trained by the product experts themselves and learn about network marketing from the most successful people in the business?"

"Sure, who wouldn't? said Linda. "But that doesn't sound very practical. I mean…"

"It wasn't," the Bag Lady interrupted. "Until satellite technology came along. But now, thousands of people coast-to-coast can participate in live, interactive video teleconferences over our satellite network, and they can do it from the comfort of their living rooms! Pretty powerful stuff, isn't it?"

"When and where can we see one of these things?" Dana wanted to know.

"How about next Wednesday night! How about right here in your apartment! And if I were you, I'd be asking myself how many people I can get to see it with me!"

Dana and Linda were impressed to the point of speechlessness. The Bag Lady took advantage of their silence to continue.

"And then, of course, there's the company's state-of-the-art voice mail system to keep you in touch with everything that's going on across the country on a day-to-day basis. And there's FAX-on-demand, so you can order any company form or literature you need and have it in your hands within seconds, instead of days. And then of course there's…"

The Bag Lady suddenly realized her students were in overload.

"Well," she said, sitting back. "You get the idea. We'll talk more about the support system later. Let's get back to our follow-up calls.

"Linda, what was the name of that friend of yours, the one you brought with you yesterday to Dana's party?" the Bag Lady asked.

"Oh, Eve. She took samples home with her. I wonder if she tried them yet?"

"I think we ought to find out, don't you?"

Linda nodded in agreement.

"Before we call her, let me share a couple of things with you about making great three-way calls. I really want you to keep in mind that even though you're just getting started, you have two extremely powerful business tools that nobody else has."

Linda looked incredulous. What could they possibly be?

"The first is 'what's happening to you right now' and second is 'how do you feel about it.' Let me explain."

"Linda, you just tried the products for the first time yesterday, am I right?"

"Right."

"And you just found out about the business opportunity then, too. So, how's it going?"

Linda thought for a moment. "Well, I feel great. I knew the product worked by the time I walked out of here yesterday..."

"And as a result, how many other people have you gotten started on the products in the past 24 hours or so?"

"Well, four, counting my kids."

"And what made you think of getting involved in the business?" the Bag Lady quizzed her.

"Well, I told you how I hated my job and always wanted to have my own business. But I guess what really did it was seeing you hand all that cash to Dana at the end of the party."

"And so what have you done about it since then?"

"I called up a bunch of my friends and they're coming over tonight for a party at my house," Linda said with obvious pride.

"Okay, so let's review: In the past 24 hours, you discovered some wonderful new products that make you feel great and when you found out you could actually make money turning other people onto them, you decided to start a business and you have 18 people coming over tonight. That about sum it up?"

Linda was smiling broadly.

"So, tell me, Linda, are you pretty excited about that?"

"I sure am! I can't believe it's all happening so fast!" Linda answered proudly.

"Exactly. It's pretty hot news, if you ask me. And so when you call Eve, let her hear that in your voice. Let her hear your pride and your excitement. Let her hear your enthusiasm! There's nothing more attractive, more magnetic than enthusiasm. That's what people really buy from you, that's what they really want—not just the product or the possibility of a business—but the feelings!

"Ready?"

Linda nodded, and with great enthusiasm, she dialed the phone.

The call went beautifully, and Linda's high spirits were indeed contagious. Eve had already tried her sample and wanted to buy a whole month's supply. At that point the Bag Lady jumped into the conversation.

"You know, Eve, I was just thinking. Instead of waiting for the company to ship your products out to you, why don't you just come by Linda's party tonight and pick them up yourself. In fact, I've got an even better idea. How would you like to get them for free?"

Eve sounded incredulous, but took the bait. "Well, sure. How would I do that?"

"It's a special promotional offer for the party tonight. Do you know anybody else who's looking for the same kind of results as you?"

Eve answered, "Yes."

"Well, if you bring five people with you tonight who get on the same program you're on, you get your products for free. Let me explain how that works."

The Bag Lady was clearly "on a roll."

"For everyone who buys, you get 20 percent off on your own purchase. So, if five people buy a program, you get five times 20 percent—that's 100 percent off. Which is another word for *free!*

"I know it's short notice, Eve. If you can't get all five people tonight, we can still talk with them by phone tomorrow. How does that sound?"

"Sounds like a great deal! I'm sure I know at least one person who'll be there with me. Let me get on the phone right away. I'll see you guys tonight!"

Linda hung up the phone with a slightly dazed look. "What was that all about?"

"That was about getting your business off to a fast start, Linda. You just set Eve up to win. Right now she's only motivated to get her products free or at a big discount. But once she sees the bigger picture tonight, and once the people she brings to the party start to get results and tell other people, she'll probably realize that she's leaving money on the table if she doesn't get involved right away."

"Of course," the Bag Lady continued. "Your business will grow regardless of whether or not Eve joins you. But unless I miss my guess, I'll bet you just recruited your very first distributor. She just doesn't know it yet."

The Bag Lady patted Linda on the back with an approving smile. Dana, meanwhile, wore an expression of delight mingled with bewilderment.

"But how does all this work, money-wise I mean?" Dana wanted to know.

"I'll explain it all in more detail tonight, after the party. It'll make more sense when we have some real numbers to work with. Basically, for every dollar spent at Linda's party tonight, each of us earns a part of it. Eve makes 20 percent commission on the people she brings, which will be applied to her purchase. Linda also will make a commission—on all the sales tonight, including a wholesale profit on anyone Eve turns on to the products. And, Dana, you also will earn money on all of Linda's and Eve's business. And I earn on all of you!

"That's the beauty of multi-level marketing. I get paid not only for teaching Dana how to do this business, but also for teaching Dana how to teach Linda, who in turn teaches Eve and so forth, on down the line. It's a wonderful concept, isn't it?"

"Amazing..." Dana replied. "I've sure never had a boss so interested in helping me make money."

"Stick with me and you'll never have to call anyone 'boss' again!" the Bag Lady cheered.

Linda suddenly realized her hour had slipped away and started gathering up her three-year old, to leave. "Mikey and I'll be back with the baby-sitter around 7:00!"

"See ya' then!" Dana called to her friend as she started searching her kitchen cabinets for something to prepare for dinner.

"Hmmmm, dinner" she thought, frowning at the meager selection in the cupboard. She'd been putting off a trip to the supermarket in hopes that her overdue child support check would arrive.

"This is going to be a challenge." She reached toward the back of the second shelf, groping around for a remembered can of tuna. Suddenly, something toppled out onto the countertop with a loud thud. Dana backed out of the cabinet to see what it was. A white paper sack, about the size of a brick, was lying face up on the counter. A scrumptious fluffy layer cake was pictured on the front. Dana remembered the Bag Lady's example about baking a cake that came out flat because an ingredient was missing. There, above the picture on the package, the name of the product was printed in large red letters:

"Self Rising Flour"

CHAPTER EIGHT

It's in the Bag!

T he Bag Lady put the next two hours to good use on the telephone, using her company's voice mail system to keep in touch with her organization and coach her distributors through the various stages of their growing businesses.

Now and then, she replayed a particularly inspiring message or dramatic testimony for Dana. Of course, just listening to how expertly the Bag Lady used the voice mail to manage her business from across the entire continent was an education in itself for Dana. She was beginning to see what an essential tool it was going to be.

It seemed like no time at all before Katie and Kevin had been fed and bathed and Linda was at the door with Becky, her baby-sitter. After a quick round of introductions and instructions, Dana, Linda and the Bag Lady were on their way across the street to Linda's place for the party.

They made a stop at the Bag Lady's car to get her big "party bag" out of the trunk, as well as a compact plastic case with a handle on top. Dana had seen her use both of these the day before at her own party, but with all the excitement and so many new things to learn, she hadn't taken much notice of them then. She was curious about them now and asked what they were for.

"I'm glad you asked," the Bag Lady responded. "Because tomorrow, both of you are going to start putting together your own. They're essentials. I don't go anywhere without them.

"This larger one," she said, hefting up a big nylon bag like professional athletes use to carry their sports gear, "is what I call my 'business bag.' Everything I need to do a party or meeting is inside." She lifted the oversized tote onto a nearby chair and opened it. It was a lively lavender color with teal trim.

"If I got a phone call that another distributor had an emergency and needed me to fill in for her at a party across town in half an hour, I could be out the door in five minutes, ready to rock 'n' roll! If I was having my nails done and all the women in the salon started asking about my products, I'd be able to do some business right on the spot.

"You've got to think like somebody who's opening up a donut shop—wouldn't you make sure your donut shop had donuts in it—and coffee, too? It's all about being ready to meet the moment in the middle. No time lost. No opportunity wasted. Bing. Bang. Boom!"

Dana and Linda gathered 'round the kitchen table and the Bag Lady showed them each item in the bag as she set up for the party.

She had a small supply of products, especially the most popular ones, which she arranged in an attractive display on a silk scarf she produced from the bag. There was also an assortment of product samples to give away or sell. The company video was in the bag, too, the same one they'd played at Dana's party and for all the people they'd visited the evening before.

The Bag Lady pulled out a black technical-looking device about the size of a package of frozen peas with two long cords wrapped around it.

"Where's the nearest telephone, Linda?" the Bag Lady wanted to know. She unwound one cord and plugged it into the back of the telephone, and the other she stuck in a wall socket, as the other two women watched, mystified.

"I know it doesn't look like much, but girls, this thing is my magic carpet. It's a speakerphone. Wait till you see what happens when we use it. You'll have people walking into your party from all over the country!" the Bag Lady promised.

There were also a few items in the bag which she didn't bring out, but showed them. Some brightly colored balloons in the company colors and a large banner with the company logo, adhesive-backed name badges and markers, sign-in sheets—these were all items she might use to set a more professional tone for regular business briefings. But for home parties, the Bag Lady didn't like to use anything that made it seem more complicated than necessary. It's important, she explained, for people to see this business as simple and easy, something almost anyone can do, anywhere.

"More or less—less is more," she assured them.

Now, she showed them the contents of the small, plastic carrying case. "I call this my Traveling Organizational File."

"It holds all of my important papers," she explained, "and helps keep me organized: Catalogs, brochures, order blanks, application forms—that kind of thing. You want all of your paper work to be neat and orderly, not dog-eared and wrinkled. That's just being your basic professional.

"And, more important, you want to know that you can put your hands on something immediately when you need it," the Bag Lady added with emphasis. "You don't want to keep a new customer waiting while you turn your world inside out searching for an order form. Believe me, you're going to be much too busy to waste time that way. That's the whole point of being organized—it frees your mind to focus on the more important aspects of your business; like spending all the money you're going to make!" she teased.

She opened up the case and showed them how she'd organized everything in neatly labeled hanging file folders.

"I personally choose folders in bright, fun colors, because that's the way I feel about my business. I don't know about you, but I just don't see myself in manila or olive drab. But whatever look you decide on for your own organizational file, make sure you really enjoy it. You're going to be looking at it a lot!"

"I love this nice recessed handle on your organizational file case. It looks expensive though," said Linda.

"Under 10 bucks at any discount office supply store. Not a major investment, considering you're basically carrying your whole business around in it."

"Now, there's one more bag you'll need to prepare before you're truly TCB—'Takin' Care of Business.'"

"Let me guess," Dana ventured. "It's got to be that saddlebag you carry around with you everywhere. It seems like you've got everything but the kitchen sink in that."

"You got it. I don't go anywhere without this. Why would I? When I get up each morning and head into my gold mine, I want to make sure I'm always wearing the right hat and carrying all the pans, picks and shovels I need.

"Now, the mining hat I wear, however, isn't on the outside of my head. It's in my mind—I think of it as the kind that has that little flashlight built in, so that whatever direction I turn my head, I can always shine a bright light exactly where I'm looking."

"The light I want to shine on everything I see is positive expectancy. Wherever I look, I see the possibilities. I see greatness waiting to be uncovered. I expect the best—which, my Dears, is exactly why I get it!

"The right tools to carry into my gold mine are in this bag of mine; the simple things I need to be an effective prospector for gold. Here's what I mean: product catalog, a few business cards, some samples with my telephone number already printed on them, and before and after pictures...

"And here, the single most important thing of all: My presentation book."

She held out a white three-ring binder with bright-colored tab dividers. It had a layer of clear vinyl over its cover, which was designed to accommodate a printed cover sheet. In this space, the Bag Lady had inserted a brightly colored flyer featuring her own before and after pictures.

"Oh, yeah," recalled Dana. "I remember you showing that book to some of the people we visited when we showed the videotape."

"That's right. I think of it as my 'storybook.' You've heard me talk about how we're all *paid storytellers* in this business. The whole thing revolves around telling stories—your own story, other people's stories. I keep all my favorite stories in this book."

The Bag Lady flipped through the binder to show Dana and Linda the kinds of things she had included. Most of the pages were actually clear vinyl protectors into which she'd inserted before and after pictures of people she personally knew, success stories she'd clipped from the company magazine, articles from major newspapers and magazines, product brochures, technical information, etc.

She used the tabs to divide the material by subject matter: Product Results, Business Opportunity, Support System and General Information. Under "Support System" she included the national and local training schedules, information on the company voice mail system and satellite network, flyers about upcoming company events, and more.

"Wow, you haven't left anything out! I definitely need to make one of these for myself," Linda exclaimed.

"That's right, you do. As I said, these are your tools, and you use different tools to connect with different people's thought processes."

Linda and Dana both looked a little puzzled. The Bag Lady knew why.

"Let me ask you both a simple question: If I wanted to teach you something, do you think you would learn more quickly by hearing about it, reading about it, seeing it, or experiencing it?" the Bag Lady posed.

The two women thought for a moment.

"For some reason," Dana offered. "I tend to absorb information better if I read it in a book, or the newspaper, or something. I probably remember more about what I learned when I see it with my own eyes,"

"Well," it was Linda's turn. "I'm thinking back to when I was finding out about this business. When I heard about it over the phone, I understood just enough to know I was interested. But I didn't really get the full picture until I experienced the whole thing in action at Dana's party. That's when I knew I was in."

"That's what I mean," explained the Bag Lady. "Different people have different styles of processing information. Some are verbal, some are sensory and some are experienced-oriented.

"Believability is another issue. Some people will readily accept the word of experts or of people they know. Others trust only their own perceptions. So, your set of tools has to offer something for everyone, for all three types.

"We have company literature and copies of articles from publications for the people who prefer to read about things. For those who like show and tell, we also have picture stories here of real people, and we also have our own personal testimonies.

"And for the experiential types, we have samples, so they can feel the products working in their own bodies. We can also allow them to experience the business by inviting them to a home party, or a satellite broadcast, or some other company event. Or we can let them listen to our voice mail or include them in a three-way call—you see what I mean? (And did you notice what I just said?)"

"You said, did we 'see' what you mean? So, you're the type of person who likes to look at things visually—right?" Dana guessed.

"Correct," the Bag Lady smiled, pleased with her pupil.

"You mean like what we were doing on the phone this afternoon—you had me experience what it was like by actually doing it!" Linda realized suddenly.

"Bingo." the Bag Lady acknowledged. Both her students were quick learners, she thought.

"Remember, I didn't just tell you what to do—I showed you. I did it with you. You got to experience what it felt like to do it right, so that later, when you're on your own, you'll be able to find your way back to that same feeling. You'll be able to duplicate it."

"I get it. You used all the different tools with us. That way no matter how dense we might have been, there was no way we weren't going to get it—one way or another," Dana laughed.

"So, what does that tell you…?"

"Have all your tools with you, all the time."

"I'm here in New York today, half way around the world from my home, but my business comes right along with me. When I have my tools, I'm always a meaningful specific, and not just a wandering generality."

"Hey, you guys, I hope we're ready. I think I hear Nadia's voice in the hall," Linda announced.

"Quick, the music!" Dana whispered, making a dive for the boom box. She'd forgotten to rewind the cassette and had no idea what the next song on the Bag Lady's "top favorite tunes" might be. It won't matter, she thought, and quickly pushed the "play" button. In an instant the room was filled with the rousing rhythms of the Pointer Sisters. It was contagious. Dana and the Bag Lady started to dance as Linda moved toward the door, bobbing her head in time with the beat as she mouthed the lyrics:

"I'm so excited!
And I just can't hide it…"

CHAPTER NINE

Chasing the Business

Within moments, the room was filled with happy chatter and bustling activity.

Eve was beaming with a ringleader's pride, surrounded by her own circle of curious friends who had accepted her invitation. Linda—the diplomat—was flushed with excitement as she scurried around greeting the newcomers and introducing everyone to each other. All told, there were 23 people in Linda's living room!

The party began the same way as the one at Dana's house the day before. The Bag Lady kicked it off, told a little about the company and introduced the videotape. This time, however, there were three personal testimonies in the room instead of just two: Dana's, Linda's and the Bag Lady's.

Then, things got even more exciting.

The Bag Lady walked over to the speakerphone and with ceremony she addressed the group.

"You've just heard about the wonderful things that've been happening for some of the people in this room. But you should also know that our business is exploding everywhere, and the same kind of excitement you just experienced is breaking out all over the country.

"To show you what I mean, we're going to call into another home party that's happening in Chicago right this very minute. I want you to hear what's been going on out there."

Then, the Bag Lady dialed a number, billing it to her calling card.

"Oh, by the way," she noted as she waited for the call to ring through, "our company has an incredible long distance plan that can save you 30 to 40 percent off your phone bill, and you also get a free calling card with it. She held up her card for everyone to catch a glimpse of it before slipping it back into her pocket. More seeds planted.

The phone stopped ringing.

"Hello, could I speak to Terry, please? Just tell her the Bag Lady is calling from Garden City, New York." The room was filled with silent anticipation.

"Hi, Terry! How's your party going?" and greetings were exchanged.

"Terry, I'm at Linda's house in New York," the Bag Lady said, looking around the room. "We have 23 people here who'd love to join you and your guests for a few minutes and hear about all the exciting things you've got going on out there! May I put you on the speakerphone?"

Terry must have agreed, because the Bag Lady pushed a button on the speakerphone and the sounds of a room full of festive noise magically filled Linda's living room.

"Hi, New York!" the entire group in Chicago roared a cheerful greeting through the speakerphone.

"I'm Terry and I've never been more excited..." Terry breathlessly delivered her brief account of why she'd gotten started on the products, what results she'd experienced and what was happening in her life as a result. Once again, there was cheering from the obviously happy crowd in Chicago.

"And I'm just getting started!" Terry added.

More whooping from the room.

Linda saw that most of the people in her living room looked fascinated, and that each time they heard the cheering in Chicago, they spontaneously smiled themselves. The excitement was becoming infectious.

"We've got 18 people here tonight," Terry continued, "and a lot of incredible stories in the room. I'd like you to meet some of my friends here..." Apparently, Terry had passed the phone to someone else. A male voice materialized.

"Hi, I'm Bill!"

Bill packed his impressive testimony into a short an' sweet, pretty powerful 30 seconds. More rowdy applause. Immediately, someone named Melissa came on the line with another exciting story, and then eight more people in quick succession. Each individual received an enthusiastic ovation. Then Terry came back on.

"Hey, everybody, are we excited!" Terry exclaimed. The room on her end of the line once again erupted with cheering. "We'd love to hear what's going on there in New York!"

The Bag Lady moved in closer to the speakerphone.

With genuine enthusiasm, she introduced Linda who was clearly a little nervous, but who quickly rose to the occasion by firing off the same testimony she'd practiced with the Bag Lady that afternoon.

The Bag Lady gestured for everyone in the room to applaud her and they were happy to join in the spirit of things. Linda was beaming as she stepped aside and Dana leaned toward the speakerphone and told her story. This time, the guests didn't need to be prompted to cheer her.

They were getting the hang of it now.

The Bag Lady returned to the phone to repeat her story for the Chicago crowd. As a seasoned veteran of the business and an experienced trainer, she'd learned to read a crowd and to adjust her repertoire accordingly. This time she focused on a different aspect of her history with the industry.

"Many of you already know me and you know my rags-to-riches story. And you already know about how I lost 60 pounds and kicked a two-pot-per-day coffee habit on these products, and how I then went on to become one of the top earning women in our industry. But tonight I wanted to share with you a different part of my story.

"One day my husband called and told me to get all dolled up, because we were going to a hotel that night. So naturally, I decked myself out in my cute little off-the-shoulder number and my strapped high heeled shoes and I pinned oleander blossoms in my hair and...off we went.

"He waltzed me into the hotel ballroom—I had no idea what to expect—and the room was full of 300 people and a big meeting was going on...

"Then some guy in a plaid polyester trousers and a brown fake-suede sport coat with white top stitching comes up to me and tells me I can make $28,000 a month!

"Now, I grew up in a New York city project and I taught first grade in Brooklyn for 10 years. I'd never in my life made more than $1,000 in a month's time. Those numbers he was spouting sounded utterly absurd to me!

"I turned to my husband and said, 'Look, buster, the Brooklyn Bridge was sold—years ago! Why are you wasting my time with this nonsense?" But he said he really wanted to try it and he asked me to just be supportive for six months—just six months...

"So, I said, 'Okay, six months.'

"Well he worked night and day, seven days a week. I never saw him anymore. And when the first check came after his first month, it was about $100!

"I phoned my father in tears, and he said, 'Follow him, he's got a girlfriend!

"But I kept my promise and when the second month's check came, it was a little over $300. Still didn't cover expenses, but—I kept quiet. Then it was $500 the third month. Not great, but headed in the right direction. The fourth month, it was up to $1,100, and then it went to $2,200, and at the end of six months, Bill's income was up to $3,800.

"Now all of a sudden, I was getting ideas. I said, 'Honey, why don't I write a nice little training program for you, so you don't have to keep repeating everything for the people and it might help them make a faster start. And let's make a nice little handbook, like I do for my first graders, and that way everything will be teachable...?

"And you know what? In another 90 days, our check doubled again! When we got that first check for over $7,000, that's when I really got it—and here's what I got.

"Number one, I got the eye of the tiger. I learned to hold my intention firmly in mind, with clarity and focus, and then pursue it with relentless, passionate commitment. No excuses. No stopping for the sale at Bloomingdales. I suddenly understood that in this life there are only reasons and results—and reasons aren't bankable.

"The other thing I got, was about learning to rewrite your goals. Coming from the poverty consciousness of my background, $28,000 a month seemed like an unreachable star, an impossible dream. But that's okay. You don't have to start out with huge goals—they just need to be your goals. You need to be able to see them, to envision them as if they were already accomplished, and own that vision for yourself and hold it dear.

"And once you've achieved those first goals, then just keep rewriting them. Whether your goal is self improvement, or financial gains, or both, 'you have to believe it to see it.' Once you can believe it and see it, anything is possible!

"Based on the stories that were shared tonight—both in Chicago and New York—you've heard plenty of proof that I'm telling the truth.

"So, congratulations to all of you on your terrific accomplishments! And to those of you who are just getting started tonight, you're in for a wonderful ride. Enjoy!"

There was cheering now at both locations as the speakerphone call ended.

The Bag Lady turned to face the group as they quieted down and, with a huge, triumphant smile, declared, "Okay, what I want to know now is, who wants to get results like the ones you heard about tonight—and who wants to make money?"

The next hour flew by, a flurry of activity. As the last of the guests straggled out the door, Eve was the only one who stayed behind. At some point during the past 30 minutes, she had completed her distributor application and launched her new business with the three customers she'd brought to the party, and two more who had not been able to attend. The latter she called from the party and they both ordered on the spot by telephone.

Eve had also booked a home party with one of her new customers.

Linda collapsed on the sofa with a satisfied sigh, as Dana and the Bag Lady toasted her with steaming cups of tea. "Great party, girlfriend!" Dana declared.

"Thank you, ladies, one and all!" Linda rose and took an exaggerated bow with mock grandiosity.

"And I would like to congratulate our brand new business partner here! Eve, it's going to be a lot of fun working together. You don't even have a clue yet, what a brilliant decision you made tonight!"

"That's right, Eve. And we'll all be here to support you every step of the way. Our highest goal is to help you be successful," Dana chimed in.

This is a perfect moment, thought the Bag Lady with a private smile. Sometimes she amazed even herself. These were the times she cherished most in her business, in her life, the times when all the gears of the universe seemed to click into place.

"So, Dahlings…, are we going to rest on our laurels, or are we going to employ ourselves?" she challenged. Everyone's attention turned.

"We still have some work to take care of tonight, but first I must tell you that I'm very, very proud of all three of you. Dana, your testimony was perfect, and I noticed how well you were planting seeds with the new customers while we were bagging up products. You're really getting the hang of it.

"Linda, you did an incredible job of getting a great bunch of people here this evening. And wow, your enthusiasm was terrific! Your passion, your excitement—these things are 75 percent of what makes a home party successful, and you had it in spades. Great job!

"And Eve, what a maniac! Look what a fast start you've made! It was only 24 hours ago that you first heard about this company, and now you've already started a business and you've made your first five sales! Imagine what could happen when you just maintain that level of performance for a month! It's incredible!"

All three women were glowing with satisfaction.

"Now, for the fun part. Let's see how much money we made!" she crowed, rubbing her hands together. They gathered around the kitchen table and the Bag Lady carefully walked them through the financial end of doing the business.

She started with Eve, explaining exactly how much retail profit she had made on her customers' purchases. And since Eve had become a distributor, she was now also entitled to get her own products at a discount. So, her total proceeds from her five customers not only paid for her own products, but also yielded her some additional profit.

"Now, Eve, that's your money and you can do anything you like with it. What I would do, if I were you, is invest in your own business by trying some of the other products for yourself. It's almost a universal in this business—you tend to sell the items you use yourself. So, bottom line, the more you use, the more money you make."

The Bag Lady turned to Linda and gave her a sly look. "Linda, Dahling, do you realize your total sales for this evening were over $1200...?" Linda's mouth literally fell open with astonishment.

"Would you like me to tell you how much money you made in the past two hours?" Without waiting for the obvious answer, the Bag Lady wrote a number on a piece of paper and slid it across the kitchen table to Linda. Linda looked down at it.

"You're kidding! Why, that's enough for my car payment!" Linda exclaimed. The other two women craned to see what was written on the paper; the figure obviously impressed them both.

"And, Dana," the Bag Lady added slyly, "I believe congratulations are in order for you, too. You just promoted yourself to executive status! In your first 48 hours, you've attained the highest earning position in the company!" It took a moment for the news to sink in.

"I did?" she squealed, both delighted and bemused. "I can't believe it!" She didn't have the faintest idea what the Bag Lady meant, but she was nearly beside herself with excitement. And it was contagious; the others were cheering and patting her on the back. She couldn't remember ever in her life feeling like such a winner before.

"What exactly does that mean?" she asked the Bag Lady when the giddiness subsided. The Bag Lady was busy poking at the keys on her calculator.

"Let me draw you a picture to make it easier: Here's your total retail sales for the past 48 hours. And here's how much you earned on that volume as a distributor." The figure obviously impressed all of them and Dana let out another little squeal.

"But it gets better," the Bag Lady continued with a smile. "At the executive level, here's how much retail profit you'll earn on that same volume from now on." This time she wrote down a significantly higher number. As Dana's eyes widened, the Bag Lady continued. "And here's how much wholesale profit you'll make whenever Linda and Eve and your other distributors sell that same amount."

"This just seems too good to be true!" Dana exclaimed again. "I've never made money like this before! And I'm having fun doing it!"

"Work is supposed to be fun—yes?" the Bag Lady asked and assured her at the same time. "Mother Theresa says *we can do no great things, only small things with great love.* When you can actually say that you love your work, and when your work also allows you to show your love for others by bringing good things into their lives—well, it just doesn't get better than that, does it?"

"I can't imagine how," Dana declared.

"And as for you, Linda, by tomorrow night at this time, I see no reason why you can't attain the same executive status as Dana. You're already three fourths of the way there. Do you feel like going for it?" the Bag Lady challenged.

"Oh, do it, Linda! I'll help you!" Dana encouraged.

"Well sure, why not! If you can do it, so can I!" Linda crowed. "What about Eve? Can we get her to the same level, too?"

"Frankly, I can't think of a better way to get you there than to get Eve there. You can qualify together. That is, if Eve wants to..." said the Bag Lady, turning to Eve.

"Well...What would I have to do?" Eve wanted to know, obviously very interested.

It was Dana who rose to the occasion. "Well, the first thing you should do is make a list of everybody you know..." she said, and repeated the instructions she herself had received from the Bag Lady just two days before.

"And then, shouldn't we do some three-way calls to follow up on those people Eve got on the products tonight?" Linda suggested.

The Bag Lady simply smiled.

CHAPTER 10
Working Your Plan

"I'd say you girls are really starting to get the hang of 'passion in action.' What you're showing Eve to do is really very simple: Use the products. Talk to people. Chase the business. It works every time," the Bag Lady encouraged.

"And speaking of planning, I like to take my direction from the best minds in the history of business, who all say; 'Plan your work and work your plan.' You need to follow a daily method of operation, and you want to commit to a fairly standard weekly schedule of non-negotiables, based on the amount of time you've decided to devote to building your business."

"What I mean by non-negotiables are the Saturday trainings, the regularly scheduled teleconferences and opportunity meetings—the things that make up your support system of scheduled events that you always do, always.

"The amount of time you commit is a personal decision of yours. And it may be different for each of you, based on your other commitments and priorities in your lives. The important thing is, to make that commitment and stick to it. Plan around it. Make your plan work for you.

"Dana, you just finished up your first 48-hour plan with a very big bang. Now, it's time to begin another, then another, and so forth. Winning can be habit-forming, you know.

Tomorrow, Linda and Eve will start their first 48-hour plans, with your help. And you already know their hair is on fire!

"Now, think about this: What if you found a couple of bright pennies like Linda and Eve every 48 hours? And what if each of them did the same thing? What kind of a business do you think you might have at the end of your first 90 days? And then imagine if you strung four 90-day programs like that together to make up your first year.

Now, can you begin to see how you could definitely finish four years with an MBA, which in *my* world stands for: Massive Bank Account...?"

The Bag Lady pulled out her Planner and showed them how she laid out her own plans for a typical month, making the most of all the regularly scheduled events in the company support system. She called their attention to a training she had scheduled for the up-coming Saturday.

"Usually, I hold a distributor training for my group back in California every Saturday morning. Since I'm on the East Coast this week, I've decided to make the most of my time here by scheduling a regional training for all my distributors in the Northeast this Saturday. Based on what's been going on with you girls, I'd consider your attendance at that training to be one of those 'non-negotiables.' Wouldn't you?"

There was no need for further discussion of the point.

Dana, Linda and Eve made their plans to work together the following day, and they each scheduled some time to make three-way calls with the Bag Lady, who would be staying in the city to take care of other business.

CHAPTER 11
Beyond the Three Rs

Just before leaving her eager new freshman class, the Bag Lady reached into her big black bag and started digging around the very bottom in search of something. With a satisfied look, her hand located what she was looking for.

She handed each of the women a small, polished wooden tile like the ones that come with a Scrabble® game. Each had the letter "R" on it, but instead of the number of points in the lower right corner like a regular Scrabble® piece, this one had a $ dollar sign.

There were mystified looks all around her, and the Bag Lady explained.

"This will help you remember the most important letter in the alphabet. When it comes to your business, it's the letter 'R'. And what this 'R' stands for, you three have already been putting into practice very, very successfully. You just didn't know it. So, before I leave, I'm going to tell you.

"The first 'R' in your business, is for Retailing. Nobody makes any money unless somebody sells something. And Dana, I know for sure that making right-now money in your pocket from your retail profits was a crucial factor for you in getting started. Without immediate cash, you wouldn't have been able to see any further into this opportunity—am I right?"

"Right—on the money!" Dana agreed smiling.

"Okay, now stay with me:

"Retailing allowed you to connect people with products, so that they could experience Results, which is the second 'R.' Results get people's attention, don't they? There are so few products in the world today that truly deliver on their promises. So, when your product speaks for itself—don't interrupt!

"On to the next 'R,' which is Refining or Repairing the programs of people who haven't experienced Results yet. This is very powerful, because people are always amazed that you actually care whether they got results or not. They're not used to that. When was the last time someone you bought anything from called you and asked how you were doing, how the product was working for you...? Right!

"So, your attitude is going to Reinforce their belief in you and your products, and it's going to solidify your Relationship. More terrific 'R' words.

"Great! Now, everybody is getting Results, and you're all Rejoicing. They're so happy, they're giving you Repeat orders. They're so satisfied, they're telling their friends, which means you get *Referrals.*

"RRRRRRRRR!" said the Bag Lady, making a sound like a souped-up racing engine.

"So, what could be better? Well, I'll tell you what—Repetition. The whole process keeps Repeating with all the new people who are Referred to you! Wow! Now, you've got quite a business going.

"But remember—another 'R'—the whole glory of MLM is building an organization. And that's easy for you now, because where better to Recruit than among all those satisfied customers you already have!

"Starting to see what you've all been doing...?"

Smiles and nods of agreement all around.

"And now, when you Recruit someone, you simply Repeat the whole process with them and teach them how to do it with somebody else—like you did, Dana, by working with Linda, who brought in Eve, who walked in tonight with a ready-made business. And so on, and so on. RRRRRRRRRR!

"What happens next is that the Royalty Override Machine—the R.O.M. kicks in—and that in turn generates Royalty income, which we'll talk more about next time. Royalty income means making money when you're not working. Royalty income means Rest, Relaxation, maybe a little Romance, and it ultimately leads to Retirement, while you're still young enough to enjoy it!

"Now, tell me if you agree. Is this not GRRRRRRRRRRRRRRRRREAT...?"

She got no argument from her three happy, smiling protégés.

Later in the evening, after bidding a weary goodnight to Linda, Mikey and their baby-sitter, Dana kicked off her shoes and slipped into her bathrobe. A moment later she stood at the kitchen sink, running water into a teakettle for a bedtime cup of cocoa.

Looking at her reflection in the paint-peeling window over the sink, she noticed that a warm smile lit up her face. It startled her a little. It was a version of her face she realized she hadn't seen much of for a long time. For the second time since she'd met the Bag Lady she found herself amazed at the change of weather in her head and heart.

It was only the day before yesterday—could that be true? She was sitting in a cab, calling herself useless, stupid, a failure. So much had happened since then. People had actually cheered for her tonight. She'd worked hard (although it hadn't really seemed like work) and she had accomplished something wonderful in just 48 hours.

For the first time in her adult life, Dana actually felt like a winner. It was such a wonderful feeling, like a miracle. And it was all because of a chance encounter in a cab on one of the bleakest days of her life. Imagine...

Someone had seen possibilities in her she hadn't even seen in herself. Someone had reminded her of how she used to feel on Christmas Eve, when magic was in the air and anything was possible. It was almost like a dream, she thought, as the steam from her cup rose up past her face.

She carried her cocoa into her bedroom and flicked on the lamp next to her bed. For no particular reason, the little ceramic jewelry box on her dresser caught her eye. It was shaped like a miniature windmill. She'd gotten it for Christmas the year she turned 13, along with the gold locket tucked away inside. It was the last gift she had received from her mother. She died without any warning less than a month later. Dana kept the only picture she had of her mother in that locket.

"I wish Mom could have seen me tonight," Dana said out loud, surprised by the sound of her own voice. "I think she would have been proud," she said, this time speaking on purpose.

She felt an urge to look at her mother's picture. She opened the little windmill.

Funny. She had forgotten there was a music box in it. A familiar melody began to play and she searched her memory for only a second before recognizing the tune. As she hummed along with the tune, she could hear the words...

"To dream the impossible dream..."

CHAPTER 12
Claiming Royalty

At exactly 9:55 A.M., Saturday morning, Dana seemed to be floating about three inches above the chair she was sitting on in the front row of the large meeting room at the Holiday Inn, near the Nassau Coliseum, on Long Island. She was flanked by Linda and Eve, who also were vibrating with excitement.

The entire front row was filled with their people, all of whom had joined the three of them in the business during the past few days, or who were interested in taking a much closer look today. Most of the seats in the second row were also occupied by people they'd invited to the training.

Exuberance filled the room. Many of the people who were there seemed to know one another and displayed genuine pleasure at being together again. There was a lot of catching-up going on, a lot of idea swapping, information sharing, business card exchanging. And an abundance of hugging.

Dana had never experienced anything like it. School was certainly never like this, she thought to herself. And work...forget it! Sitting in a classroom or an office had always been boring for her. And her limited exposure to other business meetings was also very different from the genuine affection and enthusiasm that surrounded her here. It was almost like a big family reunion, or a wedding, she thought. It was like a celebration.

At the stroke of 10:00 A.M. the room became quiet as a pleasant looking young man of about 30 years of age stepped up to the microphone on the raised platform at the front of the room. Dana thought he seemed an unlikely master of ceremonies, with his long blond ponytail, wire rimmed glasses and a well-trimmed beard. He wore jeans along with a denim shirt, a tan leather jacket with fleece on the inside, and a brightly-colored, playful-looking tie with cartoon characters on it. Unceremonious, to say the least, but the overall effect was neat and obviously an honest expression of his personality.

He began to speak. His voice was somewhat soft and quite deep, but full of passion and conviction.

"Good morning, everyone, and welcome. I'm very excited for all of you who have joined us here this morning, because I believe today is a day that's positively going to change some lives. We've got a rare opportunity to be trained by someone who's generally regarded in our industry as 'the trainers' trainer.' I've had the great privilege of working with this person, and I can tell you with total confidence, she deserves that distinction—and many others as well.

"By the time you walk out of here today, I expect you'll be seeing your business—and probably your life—on a higher level. What's more important, you'll know exactly what to do about it.

"It's been said that our presenter speaks the truth—wantonly. All I can tell you is that whenever she speaks, I listen, and so do literally tens-of-thousands of others around the world. And what I learn from her, has the wonderful habit of always showing up on my check! So, I suggest you take very good notes!

"Ladies and gentlemen, fasten your seat belts. Snap your helmet straps. And start your engines, Rrrrrrrrrrrrr! You're about to learn from the best in the business, the number one top distributor in our company, a multi-million dollar volume producer who, in spite of all her accomplishments, would still rather you all just think of her as...the Bag Lady!"

The room virtually exploded with applause. Everyone jumped to their feet as the Bag Lady approached the podium. Meanwhile, Dana poked Linda, who looked back at her with an expression of wonderment that matched her own. They hadn't realized that they'd been working with somebody so famous! There were hushing noises as the cheering subsided and everyone sat down.

"You know, I still pinch myself every time I stand in front of a room like this and fully realize the miracle that's happened in my life. It is such a tremendous honor for me to get to tell you about these products and this business, because I know that what's happened to me could also happen to you. It's such a privilege for me to get to be with you and train you on how to make the most out of this opportunity, because I'm still a teacher in my heart, and for me, teaching is the highest calling there is.

"There's an old saying that if you give a hungry person a fish, you feed him for a day. But if you teach him how to fish, you feed him for a lifetime. That's what I'm here to do today. That's what I'm in this business for. I know the only way anyone can be successful in this work and in this life, is to teach other people 'how to fish.' Everything we do to build our businesses is based on helping our people learn how to reach their goals and make their own dreams come true.

"I taught first grade for 10 years in Brownsville, Brooklyn, and I truly loved it. I'd like to share with you something I used to do with the kids to help them develop their self esteem. I'd ask them to go through magazines and newspapers and cut out pictures of eyes—big eyes, little eyes, old wise eyes, all kinds of eyes. And then I'd give them each a tin can and we'd paste all those pictures of the eyes onto the sides of the cans. Then we'd put some dried beans in each can and seal them back up.

"When they were finished, each of them had his or her very own **'eye can.'** I wanted each of them to shake those cans and make some noise to etch those two little syllables into their consciousness. I *can!*

"The first job for each of us in this room, is to burn those words into our own hearts and minds—I *can*. And to help the people we work with to own those words for themselves—I CAN!

I *can* rewrite my own life story.

I *can* leave the past behind.

I *can* own my own business.

I *can* be my own boss.

I *can* give myself and my family the abundant lifestyle we richly and rightly deserve!

"But..., I happen to know that for some of you in this room, just believing those two little words once seemed an almost impossible dream.

Just then, Dana felt sure the Bag Lady was talking about her. And she wasn't the only one who felt that way. The Bag Lady looked around the room as she spoke, making direct eye contact with one person after another. It seemed as if she knew them all.

"As a matter of fact, I remember a time when those two simple words, I *can,* were almost lost to me, too. There was a time when I used to sit in front of the TV with the channel clicker, searching for something—anything—other than my life story," the Bag Lady said this with a twinkle. She was switching gears, moving seamlessly into a more humorous mode, something she thoroughly enjoyed doing.

"Of course, I looked a lot different then—back in the plump ages, 60 pounds ago. I used to tell people I was built for comfort—not for speed. Bear in mind now, I'm still under construction." There was a chuckle or two in the room.

"My goal now is to wear either a size 9/10 or an 11/12, depending on how much breath I want to hold in that day. I want to find out what it's like for my arms to stop moving when I do." She had most of them laughing now.

"I used to be one of those women who lied to the flight attendant in first class. When they were handing out those little boxes of Godiva chocolates, I'd tell them I was a Jewish-Catholic, I had 12 children, I'd been away on business for more than a month, rushed through the airport, couldn't stop to get any presents, and could I please have more boxes of chocolate, so my children could each have a piece and not be disappointed.

"I tried all the diets, of course. When I opened up one of those little prepackaged diet meals, I thought (I prayed!) I was only looking at the appetizer. There was this tiny little piece of chicken in it. I said, 'Okay, that will fit in one of my cavities. Now bring me the rest of the chicken!' Finally, I just gave up and told my husband it was 'lights out forever,' and started wearing my robe to bed.

"You know, there's this misconception out there about fat people, that they're always cheerful, jovial souls. Apparently, that didn't apply to me. My husband was convinced I had a permanent case of PMS. When I finally got on these wonderful products, he went around the house taking down the garlic from over all the doorways.

"But fat wasn't bad enough—we were broke, too. Obese and O'busted! In fact, it was worse. We were $250,000 in debt—one-quarter of a million dollars down! Somebody told me there was a light at the end of the tunnel. I thought to myself, 'Yeah, and it's probably a train.' It wasn't until I got the results on the product that I understood that the light at the end of the tunnel represented my ticket to freedom."

The Bag Lady had the group in a relaxed, happy state of mind, ready to absorb anything she put out there. That was the whole point of making them laugh. She believed people didn't learn well when they were too serious. Learning shouldn't be hard work—it should be fun.

Dana was amazed. She'd never seen her mentor so "on" before. The Bag Lady was larger than life. Dana felt very proud to know her.

The hours flew by and in what seemed like no time at all, it was almost 4:00 P.M., the time the training was scheduled to end. The Bag Lady had covered vast amounts of information and Dana's steno notebook was nearly full.

Much of what Dana had learned directly from her sponsor had also been covered for the benefit of all the new people. Even so, she was glad for the repetition—another 'R' she thought with a smile. It served to reinforce—there we go again, she smiled even bigger—and deepen her knowledge.

During the breaks, Dana spent her time getting to know the people in her local support system, finding out where and when their meetings and trainings took place, and pumping them for their favorite business building techniques.

Everyone was friendly and eager to share what they knew. Stuffed into her notebook, Dana now had stowed samples of flyers, ads, telephone scripts, Thank You notes, and ideas for "things to say" which the more experienced people had been using successfully. And telephone numbers—she'd gotten lots of people's telephone numbers for future three-way calls and home party speaker phone call-ins.

Her head was absolutely swimming.

The Bag Lady was still going strong as the day wound down around her. She seemed to have so much more that she wanted to squeeze into the training, even though she knew that every one had gotten just what they needed—and more.

"Before this day comes to a close, we have some very important business left to take care of," the Bag Lady announced.

"When I scheduled my trip here to the East Coast, my intention was to attend to some personal business matters and spend a little time with my family. Although many of you know me well enough to know I always take my business with me no matter where I go—I really wasn't expecting to recruit any new distributors while I was out here.

"But I hadn't been here one rainy day, when I happened to share a cab with a wonderful young woman who was just about at the end of her rope. She was actually wearing it around her neck when we met." The Bag Lady looked at Dana with a smile, checking her face with a laugh to make sure it was all right to share her story with the group. Dana smiled back through the tears that were suddenly and quite clearly forming in both her eyes.

"But Dana's one of those people who doesn't just let go when she comes to the end of her rope. She ties a knot or two in it and hangs on for dear life—because life is dear to Dana. I just so happened to be the lucky person who found Dana when she was ready to be found.

"That happened this Monday. Two days later, Dana finished up her first 48 hour plan by qualifying for Executive. Yesterday, Dana helped two other people—Linda and Eve—(and she pointed to each of them in the front row) to achieve what she herself had accomplished. And today, just five fast days after that memorable cab ride—and more than 10 pounds ago, too!—almost all of the people in these first two rows are partners with them in their brand new business."

The whole room was cheering and whooping and whistling.

The Bag Lady asked Dana, Linda and Eve to join her at the front of the room up on the stage, as the ovation continued, now stronger than ever.

The Bag Lady reached into her ever-present bag and retrieved three small, glittering objects.

"Ladies, we've talked over the past few days about that wonderful fairy dust that turns this business into a magic kingdom, called 'royalty overrides.' Dana, Linda, Eve—you are now in position to claim royalty for yourself. So, it seems only right that you should each have your own crown to help you remember this day."

Ceremoniously, the Bag Lady presented each of them, one by one, with a small, rhinestone tiara made to fit a Barbie doll. As she did so, she gave each one a big hug as the crowd continued to cheer them all. Then, like a human wave, all of their guests in the first two rows stood up for a standing ovation. The rest of the room followed immediately.

Dana was completely overwhelmed with the experience. She suddenly realized she should probably say something as the applause died down—thank the Bag Lady for all her help, share how she felt, offer some words of inspiration to the group—but the very idea terrified her to her very core. Every muscle in her body wanted to sit back down in her chair *now* without speaking a word.

But then, the voice of Eleanor Roosevelt came into her head as she recalled her words from a tape she'd been listening to in her car.

> "You must do
> the thing you think
> you cannot do."

Dana remained on her feet. Shyly, she stepped up to the microphone. Her knees felt pretty shaky, but she was still standing. Her mind was a total blank. She had no idea what she was about to say. But she opened her mouth to allow words to come out—and they did.

"I've never made a speech before. I've never had anybody cheer for me before, either. I've never even dared dream of having my own business before, and I certainly never thought anybody would ever help me do it.

"And now…, it's all happening. And the only thing I can think of to say, doesn't really sound like very much, but I mean it with everything in me. Thank you."

She turned to face the Bag Lady. "Thank you, so very, very much!"

And in the silence between when Dana finished speaking and the room erupted in cheering applause, if you were listening very carefully, you would have heard the Bag Lady whisper, "Yes!"

CHAPTER 13
The Test

When Dana reached her front door, she felt like she was in an altered state. Her heart was over-flowing with all kinds of new and wonderful feelings, and she thought the top of her head would fly off any moment from the pressure of so many new ideas spawning. She was still smiling as she turned her key in the lock.

When she stepped inside, it was strangely quiet. Something was wrong! The kids were usually much noisier at this time of day. So close to dinner. She had a growing, funny feeling in her stomach. She didn't like it.

"Cindy!" she called out. No answer from her baby-sitter.

She walked into the kitchen, searching. Immediately, she spotted a note on the kitchen table. Thank goodness, she thought, breathing a sigh of relief. They probably just went for a walk.

She read:

"The kids went with their dad. He said you knew he was supposed to take them on a trip. He packed some clothes and things for them. Hope it's okay. Call me. Cindy"

Dana felt like she'd been kicked in the stomach and sank to the floor. How dare he! How dare he!

She was on the phone in an instant.

"Cindy, I can't believe you let them go with him! He lied to you. I don't know anything about this!" she raged.

Cindy didn't even try to defend herself. It had seemed suspicious to her at the time, but he was so insistent. She knew now she should have stood up to him, but she was scared.

"Cindy, think. Did he say where he was taking them? How long they'd be gone? Please, please try to remember!"

The custody agreement gave her ex-husband the right to spend every other weekend with his children, but he seldom saw them, especially since he'd fallen behind in his child support payments. And he'd never, ever taken them anywhere overnight. There was something very wrong here—very wrong.

When Dana hung up the phone she knew little more than she had before. He had mentioned something about a lake. That was all. She sat down at the kitchen table, too stunned to act. Something very confusing and upsetting was going on inside her.

Old familiar voices were lecturing her:

"This never would have happened if you'd stayed home with your children where you belong. You wouldn't be in this mess if you just could have made your marriage work. He wouldn't have left you if you hadn't let yourself get so fat. You're a bad mother—you don't even know where your children are. You should have been here. You should've been here. You should have been here."

She couldn't think. But she had to think. Where would he have taken them? What should she do?

Suddenly, she remembered something about a lake, a timeshare his brother owned on a lake somewhere in Pennsylvania. What was the name of it? She started pacing the kitchen floor. She thought of all the news stories she'd seen on TV about kids who were abducted by a parent and just disappeared—never to be found. Would he do something like that? No...would he?

She dialed 9-1-1. The policemen she spoke to wasn't very helpful. Her ex had visitation rights. It wasn't clear whether this incident even constituted a violation. She'd have to file a complaint with the judge on Monday. Nothing!

She searched frantically for the number of the attorney who'd handled her divorce. When she finally located it, she only got a recorded message on an answering machine.

Her rage was beginning to wane, and in its place a feeling of powerlessness was growing. What a way to end this wonderful day, she thought. Boy, what a fool she'd been. She really had herself convinced there was some way out of this mess she called her life. But she was a loser after all. Always had been. Always would be.

Bitter tears overtook her now, and she surrendered to them completely. She went into her bedroom and threw herself sobbing on the bed. She felt so totally alone. How she wished her mother were here. "Please, Mama, tell me what to do...?"

Impulsively, she picked up a pillow and threw it across the room. It landed with a clatter on the dresser, knocking several items over. One of them was the little windmill jewelry box. As its lid toppled off and onto the floor, the little box resumed its song, exactly where it had left off last time it was opened. Once again, the words of the song found their way into Dana's mind, this time resonating with a powerful new meaning...

"...to try, when your arms are too weary, to reach the unreachable star."

Something stirred. Something powerful and sure.
The new Dana...?
She got off the bed and went back to the phone. She started making calls, uncovering leads, jotting down notes as she went along. Within the hour, she had figured out the name of the lake, located the right timeshare developer, and identified which unit her ex had reserved for the coming week.

She called Linda. Asked her to come with her to the lake to retrieve the kids. Like a true friend, Linda cleared her plans for the evening and got someone to watch Mikey, while she sprang to Dana's assistance.

Next, Dana called the police department in the community where the lake was located. Although they weren't willing to go get her children away from their father without a court order, they did agree to be on hand and maintain order when she arrived to confront her ex.

She told them she'd be there in one hour and a half—exactly.

When Dana and Linda arrived in the small lake community, it was already dark. As planned, they stopped at the local police headquarters to let them know they were on their way up to the condo. Dana was strangely calm as she drove the winding road around the lake. She located Unit 9-B, parked the car and approached the door with a steady resoluteness. Linda was right behind her as she knocked on the door.

The disheveled man who answered the door was completely taken by surprise. He seemed more than a little frazzled by the labor intensive task of playing parent to two small children. Through the open door, Dana could see Katie jumping up and down on the pull-out sofa. Kevin was on the floor in a diaper and T-shirt, contentedly chewing on a baseball mitt.

"Dana! I wasn't expec...I mean, how did you find us? I was going to call you with the number later..." he stammered, clearly a bad liar and still in shock from seeing Dana at his door.

"Listen, Gary, and listen very closely, because I am only going to say this once. I didn't come here to fight with you. I refuse to put the kids through that. But you had no right to take them on a trip without my permission. You know it—and I know it."

Gary began trying to justify his actions, but Dana stopped him in his tracks.

"I don't want to hear about it Gary—and I will not hear about it now."

Dana hardly recognized her own voice. She didn't think she'd ever sounded so sure of anything in her life.

"This isn't the time or the place and I am in no mood. I'm taking the kids home with me right now, and we can talk about it, all you want, next week."

"The kids are staying here with me for the week," he objected. "It's our vacation. A father's got a right..."

"Fathers have rights and responsibilities, Gary. If you want your rights, then start being responsible. Frankly, you haven't lived up to either. If you want to start making some changes and be a better father, great. We can talk about that, too. But right now, you have no business dragging these kids up here. I intend to take them home now."

Gary thought for a moment, weighing his options. "And what if I say 'No?' What if I say they're staying here with me?" he challenged.

"Then I'd say you'll be at a serious disadvantage when we go back to court to renegotiate our custody agreement. I've already got a call in to my lawyer. We can work things out with him or without him. Doesn't matter to me. What's it gonna be, Gary?" said Dana, looking him directly in the eyes without blinking.

Gary looked at Dana as though he'd never seen her before. Then he looked over at Linda, who returned his stare without flinching. He looked back at Dana with a conflicted expression and was just about to say something when a police cruiser appeared in the road, passing by at a crawl to observe whether any keeping of the peace was in order.

Gary turned back into the room.

"C'mon, kids. Your mom's here to take you home."

CHAPTER 14
The Bag Lady's Secret

Dana had always been partial to Sunday mornings and this was one of her best ever. When the Bag Lady called at 10:00 A.M., she was already laying out an attractive brunch for the cheerful crew at her table. Linda and Mikey had joined with her and the kids to celebrate the week's events.

"Oh, you beat me to the punch! I was going to call you a little later to say good-bye. You're heading back home today, aren't you?" asked Dana.

"I'm leaving tonight," the Bag Lady acknowledged.

"I thought I might stop by before I head to the airport. There's one more little secret I wanted to share with you."

"Oh, that'd be great. I've got something I'm dying to tell you about, too!" she said, winking at Linda. She put her friend on the phone to say good-bye to the Bag Lady, knowing that Linda had plans for later that day.

The Bag Lady arrived in mid-afternoon in her usual boisterous good mood. After a warm hug, they settled themselves at the kitchen table over a couple of mugs of herbal tea. Dana couldn't wait to tell her about the incident with her ex-husband the previous evening. And she did, with step-by-step detail.

"You know," Dana confided, "If he'd pulled that stunt a month ago, I would have never found the guts to take him on the way I did. I would've just wrung my hands and waited for him to bring them back—if he ever did—beating myself up the whole time.

"But I remembered something you said to me one day when I was feeling sorry for myself. You told me there are no victims—only volunteers. You said no one can make you feel inferior without your consent. Meeting you has really changed me. I owe you a lot."

The Bag Lady was just a little teary-eyed as she responded.

"Dana, I don't believe there are any accidents. You were ready for a change in your life. You're the one who had the courage to accept the opportunity when it was offered. I just happened to be the one who had the privilege of showing up at that particularly perfect moment in time."

Dana reached for her hand and held it in both of her own. "I'm very glad you did."

"Me too," responded the Bag Lady.

"So, did you enjoy the training yesterday?"

"Incredible! Absolutely incredible! But you must be exhausted after a day like that!"

"Are you kidding! I'm never more alive than when I'm on my feet training a new group like that. But you know, there's one very important point I didn't cover in the training and I wanted to be sure to share it with you before I leave," said the Bag Lady.

"Well, I'm very glad you thought of it," said Dana.

"Me, too," agreed the Bag Lady. "Oh, and before I leave, I also wanted to make sure you know how to reach me at all times."

She pulled out her business card and held it so Dana could read the numbers printed below her telephone number.

"This is my voicemail number with the company. I want you to call me every single day and let me know how you're doing. I check my messages several times a day, so you can always get in touch with me this way.

"And, when I tell you what I have planned, you'll understand why it's especially important that we talk often during the next couple weeks," added the Bag Lady mysteriously.

"What?" Dana couldn't wait to hear.

"Well, now that I've seen how seriously excited you are about your business, we're going to really turn up the volume. I'm going to be running some local ads and a direct mail program in this area which will generate lots of responses, and I'm planning to send many of the leads for the New York metropolitan area to you!" explained the Bag Lady.

Dana's face was a mixture of wonderment and terror.

"Don't worry," the Bag Lady reassured her. "I'll teach you how to handle them. We'll call the first 20 responses together until you get comfortable. Trust me, this is going to be huge!

"And before you know it, you'll earn enough money to buy yourself a computer, and then I'll teach you how to use the Internet in your business. Talk about a power tool!"

The Bag Lady pointed to one additional set of numbers on her business card. "A computer will also give you another way to stay in touch with me. This is my e-mail address."

The Bag Lady could see that Dana was beginning to look a little overwhelmed.

"Relax, Dahling, for now just concentrate on getting yourself a speaker phone, like we talked about. That alone can make you a fortune," the Bag Lady reassured her..."Now, let me get back to that secret I was going to tell you."

"I consider it *the* secret to my success. In fact, it's so important, that unless you remember this one thing, nothing else I've taught you means a thing."

She really had Dana's attention now 120 percent. Dana was thinking what on earth could it be?

She grabbed for her notebook, anxious to write down the secret with perfect accuracy, while once again, the Bag Lady was rummaging in her bag as she continued talking.

"You must promise me you'll look at this every single day, and prize what you see there as the most precious of treasures in your entire world. This one thing makes your business—and your life—special and unique, like none other in the whole world," she said, still rummaging.

"This one thing is ultimately the single most important factor that will determine whether you're a success or a failure, prosperous or poverty stricken, happy or miserable."

And with that, the Bag Lady handed Dana a small flat object in a black felt slipcase with a drawstring bow. Carefully, Dana untied the cord and turned the case on its side to let the contents slide onto the table.

It was a mirror, an ordinary pocket mirror!

Instinctively, Dana held up the mirror and, at first, looked solemnly into its surface. But quickly, her own face smiled back at her.

After a silent moment, the Bag Lady quietly spoke. "And now, Dana, Dahling, you know the greatest secret of all."

"There's no woman in network marketing more powerful than Sandy Elsberg. Sandy speaks with complete and total conviction. Her entire mind, spirit and body are in this business. She cares about people. She cares about you. She knows retail better than anyone. She retails more than anyone else. Her whole essence emanates retail and nobody can build a larger organization of retailers around this country better than Sandy Elsberg.

She's a veteran of the business but everyday she approaches the business like it's the first day of the rest of her life. She's the best teacher in the business because she understands how she got where she is, and if you understand how you got where you are, then you can teach others how to get there. Sandy shows others exactly how to do it.

She's emotionally involved, she's intellectually involved and she comes to the business from the depths of her soul. She's a product of her mentors and her life experiences, and she works harder than any other person I know.

What a commitment Sandy Elsberg has made to the distribution force! Sandy is so generous, she trains people even if they're not involved in her particular organization. She is the most generous person, the most powerful person, and the best teacher I know.

She is a person who I believe is going to be in the history books when the history books are written about Network Marketing. Sandy is a woman who has defined Network Marketing in the 1990's."

—Jerry Rubin, November, 1994

About the Author

Sandy Elsberg...

Among colleagues, Sandy is often lovingly referred to as "The Bag Lady" (although the bags she carries these days, more often than not, display names like "Bergdorf's or Saks). It's a trademark she treasures. She earned it in the streets of the Network Marketing World, armed with a can-do attitude, an indomitable sense of humor, and always with a couple of well-stocked bags of sales tools and product samples that allowed her to conduct business at any and every opportune moment.

Here are a few milestones along that "road less traveled," which describes Sandy's life-journey to date:

- Widely considered "the trainer's trainer" in Network Marketing, she regularly lectures with the Upline® Masters, a circle of industry greats which includes the likes of John Milton Fogg (who fondly refers to Sandy as "the divine Ms. E"), Big Al (Tom) Schreiter, Richard Brooke, Jan Ruhe, Russ DeVan, Mark Yarnell, Dr. Charles King and other MLM luminaries. Known for her unique style which melds crackling wit with unabashed nurturing, she considers herself a shot of estrogen in a predominately male group.

- She's been quoted in *Success* magazine, and her rags-to-riches story is woven throughout the pages of *Wave 3, Your First Year In Newtork Marketing,* and *Who Stole the American Dream.* She's also a contributing editor to the Upline® journal, *MLM Insider, Profit Now,* and other key industry publications.

- Born and bred in New York, Sandy credits much of her hard-earned wisdom to her ten years of experience as an elementary school teacher in a Brooklyn ghetto. She's also an experienced massage therapist and colon health practitioner.

- With more than eighteen years in the Network marketing industry, Sandy has trained tens of thousands of distributors around the country for numerous companies in Network Marketing.

- Sandy resides in Dove Canyon, Orange County, California, with her two daughters, Eleah and Anna, a very cute puppy named Buttons, and assorted other pets. Sandy hopes you enjoyed reading the Bag Lady's story and that this book will be the beginning of a continuing dialog with you, her readers. It's her belief that MLM, like no other industry in the world, is steeped in all the magical qualities that make for great storytelling...drama and excitement, challenge and opportunity, conflict and adversity, courage and heroism.

Dahling, can we talk!?

"—If putting a financial wall around your family is important to you...

—If you care, like I do, about the company and products you put your name behind...

—If you would like to love what you are doing so much that you would do it without pay...

—If you would like your life to impact those around you and make a dramatic difference...

—If you see the wisdom of investing your energy into something that will leverage your time and money into an on-going residual income..."

"I'll show you how to create your financial destiny!"

You CAN Live Your Dreams! But Dreams Need Action—So Call, fax, or Email Now!

ph. (888) 301-2922 fax (888) 301-4964 info@sandyelsberg.com

Name

Phone Number

Address

FAX Number

City, State, Zip

E-mail Address

ITEM #	DESCRIPTION	QTY	PRICE	TOTAL
1001	BREAD WINNER BREAD BAKER by *Sandy Elsberg*		14.95	
1101	PASSION, PEOPLE, PRODUCT, & PROFIT by *Sandy Elsberg* – tape set (2)		19.95	
1301	Fat? Tired? Broke? Can we talk? by *Sandy Elsberg*		34.95	
5001	The "R" Factor — booklet and tape set		24.95	

Credit Card Number ———————————— Exp Date—

Name as it Appears on Card—Please Print—

Drivers License # ———————————— State—

Authorized Signature—

Make Checks Payable To: "Elleanna International"

TOTAL	
Total	1.
Freight $5	2.
Add 1 & 2 **TOTAL DUE**	

☐ Credit Card   ☐ Check   ☐ Cash

"Sandy gives freely from her heart and empowers people to duplicate her success. My husband and I have already earned over $750,000 from working with Sandy." —Dana McElroy

"Working with Sandy has been a gift. She has helped me progress my business to a level I could have only dreamed of! I feel very fortunate to be able to work and learn from the best—Sandy Elsberg. An incredible mentor." —Casey Decleene

"Sandy creates a tidal wave of momentum wherever she goes. She is all heart—she trained me, taught me, and helped me every step of the way to financial independence." —Daniel Bushnell

E X P E R I E N C E   C O U N T S
•**Million Dollar Earner** • **18 Year Veteran**
•**Author of MLM Best Seller** • **Featured in Wave 3**
• **The Trainer's Trainer** • **Master at Duplicating Leaders**

Sandy Elsberg Will Show YOU How to Make a Fortune!
Attend one of her phenomenol
Bread Winner Bread Baker Seminars
If you wuld like your company to host a seminar or have Sandy speak
at your convention, please call

FOLD AND TAPE HERE